GULLS
an ecological history

GULLS
an ecological history

Frank Graham, Jr.

Photographs by Christopher Ayers

 VAN NOSTRAND REINHOLD COMPANY
NEW YORK   CINCINNATI   TORONTO   LONDON   MELBOURNE

First published in paperback in 1982
Copyright © 1975 by Frank Graham, Jr., and Christopher Ayres
Library of Congress Catalog Card Number 81-50574
ISBN 0-442-22920-8

Printed in the United States of America
Design by Bernard Klein

Van Nostrand Reinhold Company
135 West 50th Street, New York, NY 10020

Van Nostrand Reinhold Ltd.
1410 Birchmount Road, Scarborough, Ontario MIP 2E7

Van Nostrand Reinhold Australia Pty. Ltd.
17 Queen Street, Mitcham, Victoria 3132

Van Nostrand Reinhold Company Ltd.
Molly Millars Lane, Wokingham, Berkshire, England RG11 2PY

Cloth edition published 1975 by Random House, Inc.

16 15 14 13 12 11 10 9 8 7 6 5 4 3 2 1

This is a book about gulls and men, not primarily a natural history of gulls, but, rather, a social history—a record of the relations between man and several of the world's forty-seven gull species.

I have chosen to write about gulls instead of humming-birds or herons or eagles because of all birds, none seems to me to reveal such a variety of effects—and countereffects—from their contact with man as gulls do. They are remarkable creatures in their own right, as I hope to show. But some kinds of gulls have been temporarily thrown out of context

Author's
Note

with their world because of man's inability to see that world in all its complexity. What has happened to these birds is related to our larger environmental problems. In all its dimensions, this is a case history in ecology.

Like anyone else who writes about gulls today, I owe a large debt to the Dutch naturalist Niko Tinbergen and his works. It is also becoming apparent that anyone who writes about gulls owes a debt to the research and observation of William H. Drury of the Massachusetts Audubon Society. I would like to thank Dr. Drury for making his material available to me, and for being additionally generous with his time and knowledge while I was writing this book.

I would further like to thank the following men and women for making my work on this book a great deal easier: Richard B. Anderson, Carl H. Bucheister, Frank Gramlich, Jeremy J. Hatch, Charles E. Huntington, Les Line, Ian C. T. Nisbet, Marjorie Spock, and Marion and David Stocking.

Several parts of this book originally appeared in *Audubon*, and I am grateful for permission to reprint them here.

A list of the world's forty-four gull species and bibliographical notes appear at the end of the book.

Frank Graham, Jr.
Milbridge, Maine

Contents

We were a curiously mixed group who set forth one morning in mid-June aboard a lobster boat into Maine's Muscongus Bay, with the means of slaughter and renewal heaped around us on the open deck. A mild breeze scarcely troubled the bay's surface. The early-morning fog dissipated itself in convoluted wisps, tinctured gold now by the pour of light from the climbing sun. Our boat moved down the bay, dropping astern the inshore islands, which were covered with dense spruce stands of an unvarying dark green. The large skiff we towed alternately lunged and heeled over in our wake.

Prologue

Our destination was Eastern Egg Rock at the mouth of the bay, but our purpose was double-edged. Steve Kress, who stood across the deck from me, his legs slightly apart and bent to absorb the lift of our buoyant craft, is an ornithologist. A tam-o'-shanter sat rakishly on his thick curly hair, and his face was bright with the thrill of something ventured. The three college students who were his assistants, two women and a tall young man, leaned on the gunwales or sat on the stacks of lumber and ceramic chimney tiles near him.

"It will be fantastic if it works," Kress was saying. "We think it *will* work. A lot of thought and preparation has gone into it."

Kress, who is on the staff of the Cornell Laboratory of Ornithology and spends the summer months at the Audubon Camp of Maine, had devised a plan to restore the common puffin, that marvelous little "sea parrot" with the bizarre, multicolored bill, to Muscongus Bay, from which it disappeared at the turn of the century. Some large puffin colonies remain off the northern coasts of Canada and Europe. But the bird now nests in rocky burrows on only two small, remote island colonies along the East Coast of the United States—Matinicus Rock, off Rockland, Maine, and Machias Seal Island, to which Canada holds a disputed claim. On this day Kress and the students were taking to Eastern Egg Rock the stuff with which to fashion puffin burrows. In a few weeks Kress would fly to Canada and receive from Canadian wildlife authorities sixty-five puffin chicks, removed for the purpose from flourishing colonies off Newfoundland.

"These tiles are seven inches square, and about four feet long, just long enough to make a good puffin burrow," Kress continued. "We want to start these chicks in artificial burrows so we can feed them and know just where they are. There'll be wire covers over the ends of the tiles to keep out gulls. And we'll hand-feed the chicks with smelts that we can buy frozen. Puffins come back to breed on the island where they were raised. We're hoping that when these chicks mature—in three or

Putting down poison bait on Eastern Egg Rock, Muscongus Bay

four years—they'll come back to breed on Eastern Egg Rock and maybe found a new colony here."

Historically, this has been a productive area for sea birds. I knew Wreck Island, which we were just passing, for I had explored it a decade earlier while I was at the Audubon Camp, which lies at the head of the bay. Wreck Island is a boreal jungle, a green riot of ferns and shrubs in a congestion of trees, heavily fertilized by the nesting great blue herons and black-crowned night herons. Its crepuscular interior is harsh with the incessant *fronk* and *quowk* of the agitated birds. But elsewhere in the bay the nesting islands are dominated by gulls—the Herring Gull, which is the common "seagull" of the East Coast, and in increasing numbers its larger relative, the Great Black-backed Gull.

And that was why we had another party aboard. Its leader was Frank Gramlich of the Division of Wildlife Services of the U.S. Fish and Wildlife Service. The division's name is something of a euphemism because the services it performs have mostly to do with the elimination of birds and mammals inimical to what man thinks are his best interests. It is the successor, its image refurbished, to the old Predator and Rodent Control branch of the Fish and Wildlife Service, and it has stamped out unwanted creatures of all kinds, from mountain lions, coyotes and gophers in the western wilderness to rats and pigeons in the less exalted wilds of eastern cities. On this day Gramlich was on a "gull control" mission to Eastern Egg Rock.

One would look a long time to find a man less likely to fit the mold of a wildlife exterminator. No one who knows him says a mean word about Frank Gramlich. He has the face of Huck Finn sagging a little at the prospect of middle age, his boyish smile is shy but infectious, his nature is unfailingly considerate. He is alert to the glories of wild things and the needless abuses to which man has subjected them. On the way to the island now he was saying that it was an old dream of his to see the rattlesnake someday reintroduced to Maine, from which man had extirpated it long ago. The state, he said, was the poorer for losing it; there was room here for rattlesnakes, as well as for puffins, bears, gulls and coyotes.

Our boat, rising now on low swells and setting gently down in broad, transient hollows, told us we had come to the region where the bay grades furtively into the sea. The cliffs of Monhegan, or else it was a remnant fogbank, rose from the distant horizon. A sail drifted leisurely between the islands like a white cloud. Gulls went by, gliding down long slopes of air, and with a graceful wingbeat or two, lifting to glide again. Eastern Egg Rock sat low in the water just ahead of us.

"I brought a bag of these sandwiches out here last month," Gramlich said, pointing to a large brown plastic bag at his feet. Inside were the six hundred or so lethal "sandwiches" which he had carefully prepared the day before, spreading seven milligrams of an avian poison called Starlicide, mixed with margarine, on each slice of bread. "I put two or three pieces on every nest, and I could see the gulls were taking them just fine. There were about a hundred gulls around, and I figured that would clean them out. Now look at them."

"There must be three, maybe four hundred of them around the island now," Steve Kress said.

Gramlich nodded expressionlessly. "It doesn't take long for others to come in and fill the vacuum," he said.

Man created an earlier vacuum on this remote island. Once a variety of sea birds nested among its tumbled rocks and low herbage. There were a few gulls, but not in such numbers as to disrupt the neighboring colonies of terns, puffins, black guillemots and several other species. But as the island's name suggests, it became a favorite place for the people on the mainland to gather eggs. Millinery gunners came to the island to kill the gulls and terns for their plumage. Other men stretched herring nets across the rocky nesting burrows of the puffins and caught them for food. Apparently the last puffin nested on Eastern Egg Rock in 1907. The other birds disappeared at about the same time.

In the intervening years some of the birds have returned, notably the gulls, but also a few guillemots and eider ducks. The terns and puffins have not. Under ordinary circumstances the entrenched legions of predaceous gulls would decimate new tern or puffin colonies in no time at all.

Our skipper anchored off the island, which is, in fact, little more than a rock, a treeless outcrop of perhaps seven acres in the northern sea, its broad, disarrayed apron of granite boulders enclosing an uplifted meadow matted with grass and herbaceous plants. Its only structure is a small wooden Coast Guard reflector mounted on the outer side of the island. The skipper untied the skiff and ferried us and our varied cargo ashore, depositing us on clumps of slippery rockweed at the water's edge. The gulls, several hundred of them, were already off their nests and wheeling, calling, above the island.

I followed Gramlich and his sack to higher ground. Yellow lichens gilded the rocks. There was the heavy odor of guano. Strewn across the upper shore was the customary flotsam—stranded crates, short lengths of rope, silvered driftwood, old timbers bearded with algae. The only unusual note in the scene was the abundance of mummied gulls, most of them "Black-backs," lying about on the rocks and turf.

With the toe of his rubber boot Gramlich prodded a dead gull onto its back. "You see, I did get a lot of them last time," he said. "The poison kills them in about two days. It destroys their kidneys, and they're probably killed by their own toxins building up in their bodies."

"Aren't you worried about an eagle or a raven scavenging the carcass and picking up the poison?" I asked him.

Gramlich shook his head. "No, there's no secondary poisoning with this substance. It breaks down along with the bird's organs, and disappears. And the sea birds which might be around don't eat bread, so it's pretty selective. But at Petit Manan, one of the gull colonies we planned to bait this year, we had to call off the project. It's the most northerly breeding colony of Laughing Gulls, and they showed up a couple of weeks earlier than usual. There are only a few pairs of Laugh-

The common puffin

ing Gulls in this area, and we didn't want to take the chance of them picking up the bait."

Just ahead of us there was a gull's nest. It sat solidly in a sharp angle of fractured rock, woven of twigs, grasses, seaweed and miscellaneous debris. In it were two eggs, slightly larger than hen's eggs, of a drab green heavily splotched with black and brown.

"Some people say you can tell the Herring Gull's eggs from the Black-back's by measuring them, but I find that it doesn't always work," Gramlich said. "There's some overlapping. But the higher you get on the island, the more likely it is that you're getting Black-backs, **because they take over the superior nesting sites on higher ground.**"

Gramlich tapped the eggs with the toe of his boot, and bright-orange yolk spilled over the nest. To his annoyance, he discovered that he had forgotten his work gloves. He thrust the thick fingers of his right hand into a small plastic sandwich bag, and using this as a makeshift glove, removed a few pieces of bread from the larger bag and spread them on the glistening nest.

"If the gulls' eggs are broken, they'll come back and eat them," he said. "And they'll gobble the bread right along with the eggs."

Gramlich moved across the rocks, treading on the gulls' eggs he found and leaving behind the poisoned bread. We walked up into the quack grass, which was densely infiltrated by angelica, yarrow, silverweed and other plants. Across the island we could see Steve Kress and his assistants piling the lumber and tiles for their artificial puffin burrows.

"This control program is no solution to the gull problem," Gramlich said as we walked through the grass looking for nests. "It's only a stopgap. But the National Audubon Society and the state Audubon societies in Maine and Massachusetts have gone along with us on this thing at a few islands we carefully selected. Something had to be done right away to save the other species from the terrific predation on their eggs and young. We included this island on an experimental basis because of the puffin project. Puffins couldn't get a foothold here with all these gulls. Look at this!"

At our feet lay a small tangle of black and white feathers, identified by its scarlet feet as the remains of a black guillemot. These relatives of the puffins re-established their foothold on the island some years ago, before the gulls built up to large numbers. The bird at our feet had been eviscerated.

"It looks like a Black-back caught this one," Gramlich said. "They turn the guillemots inside out, like an old glove."

We watched a guillemot sputter out of its burrow in the rocks just below us. Like others of its kind, it was a weak flier and had trouble getting airborne. (They catch rock eels and other small fish by diving beneath the surface, and as E. E. Cummings said of penguins, "Their wings are to swim with.") The guillemot below us would have been an easy mark for a persistent gull. Its stubby wings flapping frantically, it hurtled toward the water, thrashing through the grass and glancing off rocks, looking more like a small boy tumbling downstairs than a bird in flight.

Gramlich searched out and destroyed the contents of more than a hundred gulls' nests. Some of the eggs were close to hatching. As they crumbled beneath the pressure of his boot I could see the pulsing contents, striated with blood vessels. It was disquieting to hear an occasional muted squeak sounding from a crushed egg.

"It's a hell of a way to make a living," Gramlich said, with an expression of abashed distaste.

It's a hell of a world we've made for ourselves and these animals, I thought as I followed him through the grass. We've thrown the whole system out of balance, and now we're forced into adopting emergency programs that are both inadequate and degrading. Gramlich had stopped ahead of me and bent to pick a golden fragment from the matted green. When he held it up, I saw it was a feather.

"It's from a yellow-shafted flicker," he said. "I find an awful lot of these feathers on the nesting islands. The gulls seem to gather them and build them into their nests. It makes you wonder if the gulls are being selective, and picking out mostly the bright-colored feathers." He stroked the feather, turning it so that it caught the light. "Or maybe *I'm* being selective." He grinned.

It was time to leave. Fog was moving in from the sea again, the distant islands dissolving behind it. We were leaving our strange cargo on Eastern Egg Rock: artificial burrows ready to receive the puffin chicks brought by plane, car and boat from another country to replace the birds our ancestors had wiped from the island, poisoned bait sown in ruined nests to "control" the gulls whose population had been swollen to pest proportions by the wastes from our careless civilization. The birds were still wheeling above us, uttering their cries of alarm. Even before we pushed off, the first of the gulls began their descent on spread wings, eager to resume brooding the eggs they had abandoned as we came ashore.

Several years ago an editor of *The Fiddlehead*, a small literary magazine published in Fredericton, New Brunswick, wrote with puzzlement and a trace of defiance about the flood of "seagull" poems that claimed a large part of his and his colleagues' attention. They had read nearly four hundred poems in the last year. "Seagull poems vie in number with poems in which the poet yearns after a designated member of the opposite sex," the editor wrote, "and with poems that have to do with windows, window frames, and quirks of perception . . . Our contributors in good number are every-

1

where moved to poetic utterance by these creatures—how they veer and soar, how they pick over garbage, how they trace patterns (God, how they trace patterns) . . ." Not knowing what to make of the phenomenon, the editors simply rejected the poems.

Gulls, like cats, stimulate a wide variety of emotions in the breasts of humans who come into contact with them. In their graceful flight, tracing patterns or otherwise, they are the essence of *bird*. They can be, and often are, compared at a distance to drifting snowflakes or to ethereal beings concerned only with the empyrean, severed from the cares and dinginess that draw buoyancy from man's lumpish spirit. They are probably the creatures that wrung from Yeats the song "I would that we were, my beloved, white birds on the foam of the sea!"

Frank M. Chapman, who was one of America's most famous ornithologists, thought that the cries of gulls are partly responsible for their hold on us. At a distance they sound a note akin to the wailing human voice, and indeed the *Oxford English Dictionary* suggests that the origin of the word "gull" is related to the old Breton verb *goelaff,* "to weep."

The Herring Gull utters a wide variety of calls—wailing, guttural and sibilant—as it goes about its business of feeding, fighting and mating. The Great Blacked-backed Gull has a deeper, more ominous note befitting its New England designation as the "minister gull," though this also refers to its dark mantle or cloak. The Laughing Gull's high-pitched cackle sometimes sounds almost maniacal, while the little Bonaparte's Gull emits a series of squeaks that always remind me of the noises coming from a rubber doll's hollow belly when it is vigorously squeezed.

I sometimes hear and see those Bonaparte's Gulls in autumn, undulating on the ebb tide just below the little cabin at the shore where I write. My window gives out on a pageant of gulls, and I never tire of watching their aerial display in all seasons and in all kinds of weather. As they rise on arched wings, my head sinks lower and stretches for-

Bonaparte's Gull

ward to follow their probe into the intense blue vastness where they seem to gather, each to itself, the sum of heaven's light. I see a Laughing Gull fly past, its cylindrical body tipped by the sharply defined black head, tapering from the neck like the warhead on a missile. Herring Gulls make their way up purposefully into the mouth of the river at two wingbeats a second, heading for the fish cannery and its wastes. Sometimes a closer look in winter proves that there are Ring-billed Gulls among them, slightly smaller birds with a more buoyant, agile flight. If I look even more carefully I may detect an Iceland Gull, its pale-gray wings devoid of the dark tips that mark those of most other gulls.

We tend to think of gulls as all too common along our coasts, but how common they are depends on the place and the kind of gull. One evening early in 1975 I received a phone call from excited friends in Salisbury, Massachusetts. A Ross's Gull had appeared offshore only a few blocks from their home. This gull, a small bird with its "hood" reduced to a black ring around its throat and its white body tinctured with rose, had never before been seen on the East Coast of North America. It is a bird of the Arctic mists whose nesting grounds remained a mystery to ornithologists until 1905. In that year the mystery was finally solved by a Russian explorer, Sergius A. Burturlin, who came upon Ross's Gulls in the Kolyma River Delta on the Arctic coast of Siberia, looking "like so many roseate points on the bluish ice of the great stream." After the nesting season this gull disappears into the gloom of the polar winter.

Now, suddenly, it had materialized not far from the city of Boston. The news spread through the Northeast in a matter of hours. Bird watchers came trooping into town from all over the country. Roger Tory Peterson, America's most renowned birder, had never seen a Ross's Gull and arrived full of years and excitement, from his home in Old Lyme, Connecticut, to add it to his life list. A bemused local policeman, besieged by strangers asking directions to the hallowed spot, confided in a reporter, "If I saw a pink seagull, I don't think I'd tell anybody about it." He was in a minority in Salisbury, which had unexpectedly acquired a tourist attraction.

Yet even *The Fiddlehead*'s quivering young poets detected the gulls' seamier side. They eat garbage. They are a nuisance at fish canneries, a hazard at airports, an unmitigated catastrophe at some breeding colonies of other birds.

Perhaps gulls in their attributes somehow remind us of—well, *us*. "In form and moving how express and admirable!" Hamlet ruminated on man, "in action how like an angel! in apprehension how like a god!" If a gull's apprehension falls short of the divine, its form, movement and action are as close to an angel's as are those of most persons I am acquainted with, and it seems to experience something like delight on a fine day and in a high wind. A gull may feel frustration and suspicion, it is often noisy and quarrelsome, it tends to get its living in the easiest possible way, and we may think, in our more fastidious moments, that it has "filthy habits." How like our neighbors!

But like all comparisons of this sort, it does not bear a very close inspection. Pantheists and allegorists excepted, it is better, I think, to feel sympathy, affection, admiration, even aversion in some cases, to species other than ours, rather than close kinship. The naturalist Henry Beston's view of wild creatures is surely the correct one: "They are not brethren, they are not underlings; they are other nations, caught with ourselves in the net of life and time, fellow prisoners of the splendour and travail of the earth."

Still, we have in a sense a tangible relationship with gulls, as we have with many other of our unreasoning fellow prisoners. We pick out those of their qualities we believe may be useful to us, and use them. It is an old American tradition that gulls benefit man in one way or another. Consider Hiawatha, for whom, as Longfellow tells us at length, gulls mounted a lifesaving expedition. The hero had set forth upon the shining Big-Sea-Water to catch the sturgeon, "Mishe-Nahma, King of Fishes." But the prey turned on the predator. The great fish leaped from the water to swallow Hiawatha, his birch-bark canoe and his little friend, Adjidaumo the squirrel. When Hiawatha smote Nahma's heart with his fist and sent him thrashing and dying onto the beach, he was left with the problem of how to extricate himself from his fleshy prison. Then, from outside, there came a mighty clamor and a flapping of wings. Looking up, Hiawatha

> *Saw a gleam of light above him,*
> *Shining through the ribs of Nahma,*
> *Saw the glittering eyes of sea-gulls,*
> *Of Kayoshk, the sea-gulls, peering,*
> *Gazing at him through the opening,*
> *Heard them saying to each other,*
> *" 'Tis our brother, Hiawatha!"*

He called to the birds to make the rifts a little larger, "with your claws the openings widen," and set him free. Now, gulls as we know them have webbed feet with claws that are no more useful to them than toenails are to us. But Hiawatha's gulls attacked the sturgeon with "beak and claw together" and ultimately released him, earning his accolade as "Kayoshk, the Noble-Scratchers," as well as an opportunity to stuff their craws with a gourmet's fish.

At a later date the Mormons saw California Gulls as an instrument in the hand of God. In 1848 the new religious colony was struggling to harvest its first food crop when the fields became overrun with wingless, long-horned grasshoppers (*Anabrus simplex,* now called the "Mormon cricket"). The voracious grasshoppers threatened the Mormons with disaster. Orson F. Whitney, in his *History of Utah,* describes the scene:

> *Just in the midst of the work of destruction great flocks of gulls appeared, filling the air with their white wings and plaintive cries, and settled down on the half-ruined fields ... All day long they gorged them-*

selves, and when full, disgorged and feasted again . . . until the pests were vanquished and the people were saved. The heaven-sent birds then returned to the lake islands whence they came.

The Mormons later erected a handsome monument to the gulls in Temple Square, Salt Lake City, "in grateful remembrance of the mercy of God to the Mormon pioneers."

However, the age of heroes and miracles is past. The utility of gulls in this duller time is mostly symbolic. Audubon ate them, as he did other birds after he had painted their carcasses wired in lifelike attitudes (he thought gulls excessively salty), but few of us look on them as food today. Eating gulls, like decorating our hats with their plumage, declined after bird-protection laws went into effect. Waterfowlers, in fact, sometimes take advantage of the gulls' protected status, mounting carved gulls on their boats as "confidence decoys." Ducks and geese, according to these hunters, are somehow aware that gulls are not shot and thus hang around them under the delusion that they, too, will come under the protective umbrella.

At least one conservationist has taken advantage of the gulls' modern population explosion, which parallels our own. During an interview on a radio program a few years ago in Boston, he wanted to describe the ills society faces because there are too many people. His host warned him, however, that the city's religious atmosphere was hostile to such ideas. Our conservationist substituted gulls for people in his argument and presumably put his message across.

A visitor to the coast may sometimes see a gull's carcass hanging from a fishing boat or a wharf, evidence that the victim was caught feeding on the jealous fisherman's catch or fresh bait and suffered the consequences. But most fishermen look on gulls with a tolerant eye. In some parts of Europe the legend lingers that gulls are drowned mariners or fishermen returned to their old haunts in another guise, and they are treated with respect. W. H. Hudson, in *The Land's End*, speculates about a more material source of the affection in which Cornwall fisher-men hold their gulls:

> To injure a gull wilfully is to invite disaster. It may be that the or-igin of the feeling is simply the fact that gulls gather in vociferous crowds around the boats and in the harbour where the fishing has prospered, and in this way become associated in the fishermen's mind with all those agreeable ideas or images and emotions connected with a good catch—smiles and cheerful words of greeting in the home, with food in abun-dance, money for the rent and for needed clothes and other good things for the little ones.

Gulls have been a part of man's consciousness for ages. But what are gulls, and how do they fit into what many of us like to think is man's world? Let us look at gulls as they are seen by some modern biologists.

"*A in't* ain't in the dictionary," our grandmothers used to tell us, and many ornithologists are equally emphatic (and just as often ignored) about the word "seagull." Gulls, they assert, are not seagoing, or pelagic, birds at all, but scavengers who prefer to live their lives close to the shore and sometimes even far inland. In this view, they are as little entitled to be called seagulls as the crewmen of harbor tugs and ferries are to be called seamen.

Perhaps, but as we learn more about the lives of gulls this reasoning becomes more uncertain. One species, the

2

Black-legged Kittiwake, spends a good deal of its time at sea, often crossing the Atlantic from its nesting colonies around the British Isles to feeding sites off North America. Gerald A. Sanger of the National Marine Fisheries Service has recently observed the regular winter occurrence of Herring Gulls and Glaucous-winged Gulls three hundred miles and more from land in the North Pacific. His records indicate that they were neither wandering juvenile birds (most of the gulls he saw were adults) nor isolated specimens following ships or blown off course by storms; other species of gulls that may follow ships were seldom if ever seen at these distances, suggesting that the flights were made consistently only by those two species, and that they had flown in the face of the prevailing winds. Sanger speculated that they had originally been lured far from land by the promise of galley scraps. Eventually they began to feed regularly on pelagic gooseneck barnacles, which they found on the floats of fishing nets or on flotsam and jetsam. In any case, a number of individuals of the two species are apparently now able to occupy an ecological winter "niche" far from their accustomed habitats along the shore.

The safest objection to the word "seagull" is that it tends to obscure just such distinctions as these, which help to make gulls among the most fascinating of animals. Most ornithologists assign gulls to the subfamily *Larinae* and lump them with their close relatives, the terns, in the combined family, *Laridae;* others separate them into families of their own. The dispute does not concern us here. As Dean Amadon of the American Museum of Natural History has written: "Of all the various categories into which living things are grouped, whether by scientists or laymen, the individual and the species are the only ones that have an objective reality in nature."

We find, then, an amazing diversity within this subfamily. In fact, gulls have helped to illuminate for us some of the most complex problems of speciation, or the creation of species, as they go about reproducing themselves on their various nesting islands around the world. A species may be defined as a population of individuals breeding among themselves but not normally breeding with individuals of another species. There are all sorts of qualifications here, and hybrids are a living proof of one of them. But in general gulls, like other animals, recognize the limits of their own species, and a Ring-billed Gull, for instance, will not be found cohabiting with a Laughing Gull.

The Herring Gull "group," however, is a splendid example of the way in which nature often scrambles and blurs distinctions. Scientists are generally agreed that a new species of animal is usually created by geographical isolation. Let us say that a group of animals is separated from its larger population by some natural event: a flock of birds is blown off course to a remote island where its members settle down and begin reproducing themselves, or a herd of antelopes is cut off by the eruption of a mountain chain or the creation of a new body of water. Adapting to their strange surroundings and breeding only among themselves, the isolated animals presumably will, over a long period, develop certain characteristics that differ from those of the great population of which they were once a part. The isolated animals become, in effect, a new species. If, after ages have passed, they somehow make contact with the parent stock again, the two groups will have trouble "recognizing" each other. They may not be able to communicate, or resume breeding, with their old congeners. In this case, they have become reproductively isolated. The splinter group forms a true species.

One of the best documented examples of speciation is that of the Darwin's finches on the Galápagos Islands. At some point in the distant past a species of finch, native to the South American mainland, reached the Galápagos. Its members spread among the various islands. Finally each small group preferred one of the islands, or one part of an island, for its habitat. Each became isolated from the other flocks. In isolation, and exploiting its own niche, each flock began to develop distinct characteristics of plumage or voice or bill. Over the ages they evolved into fourteen separate species.

The so-called Herring Gull group did not spread out so neatly. For a number of years the argument went on over whether various northern gulls were distinct species or merely subspecies of the Herring Gull. Apparently ten or fifteen thousand years ago there was a single species, the ancestor of the current ones, living around the Bering Sea. Over a long period this single species began to travel both east and west from the Bering Sea, breaking up into smaller populations and settling in comparative isolation. As they spread and lost contact with each other, these individual races developed minor differences. One population, which we now call the Herring Gull, spread east across northern North America and the Atlantic and finally overlapped with another population of the original species. The latter, which we now call the Lesser Black-backed Gull, had spread through Siberia to western Europe. The two birds were by this time quite different in their plumage, the Herring Gull wearing a light-gray mantle and the Lesser Black-backed Gull a dark one. Though they occasionally hybridize today, the two gulls are recognized as distinct species. Their voices differ, so that they are no longer able to communicate with each other. Their habits differ too. The Lesser Black-back migrates south in the winter to the Mediterranean Sea and Africa, while the Herring Gull wanders only briefly and irregularly in what are not true migrations. One of the barriers to successful matings between these two species is a lack of synchronization. In regions where their breeding ranges overlap, there is a difference of two weeks or more in the start of their egg-laying periods. Presumably, then, there are other aspects of their breeding cycles that do not ordinarily mesh.

But the differences among some of the other Arctic gulls are not so clear. For a long time there were ornithologists who believed that the California Gull was a subspecies of the Herring Gull. Certainly they look much alike (the California Gull is slightly smaller) and they sometimes breed in the same area. But in the middle 1950s Martin H. Moynihan studied California Gulls nesting alongside Herring Gulls on Pelican Island in Manitoba's Dog Lake. There was occasional hostility

Ring-billed Gull

between the two alleged species, with the Herring Gull proving to be the dominant bird, but no other contact. Moynihan concluded that "the apparent absence of sexual or 'friendly' social reactions between the California Gulls and Herring Gulls on Pelican Island would strongly suggest that the forms are now separate species."

Even more complex questions were tackled in 1966 when Neal Griffith Smith published the results of his studies on the evolution of some of the large gulls breeding in the eastern Canadian Arctic. At one time these gulls had formed a single species. During the long epoch of glaciation they fragmented into isolated populations. One of the birds that Smith studied was the Herring Gull, white-bodied with gray wings and black-and-white wing tips. Two others, the Kumlien's Gull and the Thayer's Gull, have had "a checkered taxonomic history." The Kumlien's Gull, white-bodied and gray-winged with varying amounts of gray in its wing tips, was at one time considered a hybrid between the Iceland Gull and the Thayer's Gull. Now it is described by most authorities as a western race of the Iceland Gull, which has a large breeding colony in Greenland. The Thayer's Gull, which looks very much like the Herring Gull, was originally considered a distinct species, then a kind of Herring Gull. Now it is recognized once more as a distinct species.

Smith wanted to settle these problems of "identity." Going further, he wanted to find out why, when these gulls are obviously so closely related, they do not interbreed and merge once more into a single species. Certainly there is every opportunity for them to do so. The three gulls nest in close proximity to each other in that area. Their postures, calls, movements and behavior are strikingly similar during courtship. Yet persistent observation over several years showed that the three species almost never interbreed. What is the "isolating mechanism" that keeps the birds true to their own species?

Traveling by plane, canoe and dog sled from one gull colony to another on Baffin Island, Smith gradually narrowed the possibilities. Fi-

Laughing Gulls

nally he concluded that the critical distinguishing feature is invariably the eye—or, to be exact, the contrast between the color of the eye or its fleshy ring and the white plumage of the head. This contrast is dark against white in the Thayer's and Kumlien's Gulls, light against white in Herring Gulls. To test his thesis, Smith used a drugged bait to capture a number of gulls of various species and both sexes. While they were still narcoticized, he altered the color of their eye rings with oil paint and a thin brush (the paint apparently caused the birds no physical irritation). Then he released the gulls so that they could return to their mates.

The results of Smith's experiments appear to be dramatic. The females, who play the major role in forming new mating pairs, choose males with "eye-head contrast" and wing-tip patterns similar to their own. By altering these characteristics on the males, Smith induced the females to choose mates of other species. But a male, even if already mated and copulating, would no longer copulate with his mate after Smith had altered her eye pattern. The change was more than psychological. Various stimuli operate to bring the male gull's testes into breeding condition. An important stimulus is the eye-contrast pattern of his mate. When Smith altered this pattern, the male's testes began to shrink. The pair invariably broke up.

Ornithologists recognize forty-seven true species of gulls, thirty-seven of which live in the Northern Hemisphere. They share many characteristics. Male and female look almost exactly alike, so that in the field one must usually observe behavioral differences during breeding to distinguish a gull's sex (though in some species, such as the Laughing Gull, the male may have a more brightly colored bill). Gulls produce what one scientist has called "semi-precocial" chicks; when they hatch, the chicks are covered with down and are soon able to walk, but unlike truly precocial young, they cannot feed themselves and they remain close to the nest.

3

Gulls are comparatively long-lived animals. There are reports of these birds living well into their forties in captivity, though there are obvious difficulties in obtaining accurate information about wild gulls. Although ornithologists affix metal bands or rings to the legs of birds to gather information about their longevity or migration routes, such devices are unreliable tools when studying birds that live on or around the sea. Sand and salt water erode the bands so that they are unlikely to last as long as the bird itself. Wild gulls, however, are known to live well into their twenties and sometimes longer. Unfortunately, the alleged record holder lost its title not long ago on a recount. In 1966 a banded Herring Gull was found dead on Lake Michigan's Little Traverse Bay. The band was sent to the U.S. Fish and Wildlife Service, which keeps banding information on file. Its staff reported that the gull had been banded as a chick by the noted ornithologist Olin S. Pettingill, Jr., of Cornell, on June 29, 1930, on Duck Rock Island near Monhegan, Maine. Pettingill proudly made the claim that this gull, thirty-six years old at its death, was the oldest wild bird on record. In 1974 someone thought to check the file once more. The Bird Banding Laboratory had, it seems, made an error; Pettingill's gull had in fact been banded by him on Lake Michigan in 1948.

At any rate, gulls are hardy, resourceful birds. Anyone who has watched a gull stand on an ice floe for hours or wade into the winter surf wonders why their legs and feet don't freeze (gulls aren't even protected by the feathery "leggings" that cover the legs of snowy owls and ptarmigans during the Arctic winter). Scientists have discovered that birds are equipped with tiny valves called precapillary sphincters which shut off blood from the warmer parts of the feet but pump it rapidly to the colder parts of the extremities. The pressure of the flowing blood produces heat, warming the bird's feet from within.

While most gulls apparently prefer to drink fresh water, they readily drink salt water as well. Otherwise they would not be able to survive for long periods on the ocean, or in the case of California Gulls, on marshes near Great Salt Lake. For a long time it was believed that the birds eliminated the salt with the help of their kidneys. But studies eventually showed that a gull would have to excrete two liters of urine to remove the salt it had ingested from one liter of sea water. Further investigation proved that salt glands, like those possessed by other sea birds, do most of the work. These glands, located under the skull and just above the eyes, concentrate the salt in a bird's body and flush it to the nasal cavity. From there it flows out through openings in the bill. The excreted salt is then flicked from the bill by the abrupt shake of the head characteristic of many sea birds.

These salt glands have wide implications in tracing the evolution of gulls and other birds. Birds evolved from a reptilian ancestor (a gull's feet and legs are sheathed in scales, its feathers are really modified scales). Thus ornithologists were fascinated to learn several years ago of the discovery in South Africa of a crocodile unearthed in Upper Triassic strata that revealed a number of birdlike structural features and may have been arboreal. Among those features were paired salt glands above its eyes. The modern salt-water crocodile gets along very well far from fresh water, as sea birds do, and one of them swam to the Cocos Islands in the Indian Ocean, six hundred miles from any other land. As the biologist A. D. Walker writes: "Living crocodiles seem, to a surprising extent, to represent a 'frozen' stage in the evolution of birds."

The orientation of gulls, even at sea, seems to be excellent. Taken as far as three hundred miles from their nests and released, most gulls find their way back very efficiently (they orient themselves more quickly on sunny days than on cloudy ones). Biologists speculate that they recognize landmarks such as islands or bays and learn to use them in finding their way home. Birds taken from their nests a second time return much more quickly than they did the first.

Certain terns are said to sleep on the wing occasionally. I know of no record of "sleep-flying" among gulls, but they are capable of other spectacular feats. Many observers have seen a gull in full flight incline its

31

head and casually scratch the back of it with an extended foot. (Peter Matthiessen, watching a shore bird perform a similar maneuver at speed over a pond, writes that it "made this attenuated bird fly like a sprung umbrella in a gale.") And the Dutch naturalist Niko Tinbergen once saw a Herring Gull, having snatched a guillemot's egg, being pursued by another gull of the same species. The pursuer was so persistent that the first gull released the egg. "The second gull immediately stalled," Tinbergen writes, "and with a rapid manoeuver seized the egg by its pointed end as it fell and flew off with it. The egg was still intact and was eventually consumed by the second gull."

The wings of some birds, like the grouse and woodcock, are short and stubby for rapid flight through dense forests, or like those of the albatross, they are extremely long and narrow for extensive soaring. A gull's wings, especially those of the larger species, strike a happy medium between the two, allowing them considerable versatility and great maneuverability in the air. A Herring Gull has been seen to pursue an osprey, and with a swift loop from below, snatch a fish from the astonished raptor's talons. They have been seen to hawk ants and other flying insects which commonly swarm over fields or water. They are able to dive, swoop and reverse themselves with the deftness we often believe is confined to falcons, swallows or hummingbirds.

But it is the gull conserving its energy, soaring or gliding on extended wings, that most often stirs man's wonder. Like a plane, the gull is able to make use of the lift produced by the difference in air pressure above and below its wings. To soar, it takes advantage of thermal updrafts. These updrafts, tall vertical columns of air, occur when the air is colder than the water beneath. (That is why the gulls are found most often far at sea in late fall and winter, when they are able to find helpful updrafts.) Gulls on motionless wings ride the columns to great heights, neatly transferring from one column to another to make headway or dropping on the downdrafts that surround them. In fact, even the "soaring" bird is really gliding downward all the time. Since it is

Foraging Herring Gulls

heavier than air and does not drift like a balloon, it circles into the air column that is rising faster than the bird is descending. As Edwin Way Teale has said, the soaring bird "is like a man walking slowly down the steps of a rapidly rising escalator."

These air columns are destroyed in winds of over forty-five miles an hour, or when the sea's temperature rises above that of the air. At such times the adaptable gull makes use of the "obstruction currents" created by the flow of air over cliffs, hills and ships. One of the best places from which to observe an airborne gull is the stern of a moving ship. Gulls, wings spread out, altering their course by a simple adjustment of their primary feathers, follow a ship for hours almost without moving a muscle, as if towed like kites on long strings. A. H. Woodcock has described the gulls at Woods Hole, Massachusetts, using the updrafts created by a high windward embankment to glide to their roosting island almost half a mile offshore. "It is amusing to note," Woodcock writes, "that, failing to reach the roosting place on the first trial, the birds will return to the region of the up-flow (while they still have enough altitude for a quick down-wind glide), rather than flap their wings for the last few hundred feet of the flight. Apparently several minutes of extra soaring time are preferable to a few seconds of flapping."

I take a personal interest in what and how a gull eats. I remember one warm spring day watching two species of gulls successively feeding in front of my cabin. Late in the morning a small flock of Herring Gulls settled at the edge of the incoming tide. There was a stiff breeze from the southwest. The water advanced in a series of gentle arcs edged with foam. The gulls moved onto the mud ahead of the tide and stood motionless, headed into the wind. Then they began to feed on sandworms, as robins would feed on earthworms on a manicured lawn. A gull would rush forward, snatch at the mud, withdraw a worm as long and limp as a strand of spaghetti, and gulp it down. If the gull made the snatch to one side or a little behind its original position, the wind ruffled its feathers, and it abruptly turned and faced the wind again. If it took a position too close to a dominant gull of the flock, the stronger raised its great gray wings, tilted its threateningly open bill upward and charged. The weaker gull retreated, then warily shuffled around into the wind.

The day, the wind and the tide receded, leaving few traces behind. The sunset was not spectacular. But in the east the clouds were blue with rain, while billows of salmon towered above and beyond them. I was about to leave my cabin when a Great Black-backed Gull landed on the shore. Audubon describes this bird:

> *Larus marinus (the Great Black-backed Gull) is so superior both in strength and courage to Fulmars, or even Gannets, to say nothing of Gulls of all sorts, that at its approach they all give way, and until it has quite satiated itself, none venture to approach the precious morsel on which it is feeding. In this respect, it is as the Eagle to the Vultures and Carrion Crows.*

This gull had spied a "precious morsel" as it flew over the shoreline. The head of a large fish had been left behind by the tide. The gull approached it. As I watched in the failing light, a crow dropped from the nearby trees and made for the fish head too. The gull rushed at the intruder, driving it off, but the crow immediately returned. The gull ignored it for the time being and went to work on the fish head, stabbing it vigorously with its heavy bill. It extracted the eyeball, then attacked the cheek. Each time it struck with its bill, the head bounced and settled a few inches away. The crow kept edging in, snatching whatever spattered from the fish head on impact.

Occasionally the gull drove it off, but the crow always returned to take up its position at the edge of the action. I couldn't help but think that the crow would have managed the business better. The crow would simply have placed a foot on the fish head, holding it down while tearing away chunks of the flesh. I could almost imagine the crow sneering at the wasteful, hammering lout. But the gull had the simplest solution, after all. It suddenly picked up the huge fish head in its bill, chomped it several times to flip it so that the tapered front end was pointed toward its own gullet, and with a mighty convulsion, swallowed the whole thing!

The gull shook its head, stood for a moment looking stunned, and finally hurried away to reach its roosting island before dark. The crow was left with not even a bone.

It is this capacity to utilize whatever is in the landscape that has allowed gulls, like the brown rat and the German cockroach, to spread and thrive. It gives them an advantage over most other creatures in a world so drastically altered by man. Under so-called natural conditions Herring Gulls, California Gulls and others function as both predators and scavengers. The latter trait has served them well in the "effluent" society, helping a greater number of young to survive the first year of their lives and swelling the population to what humans prefer to think is pest proportions.

Hunger is seldom a problem for mature gulls. They have an uncanny knack of searching out food with the utmost efficiency. The habit of certain crabs of burying themselves in the sand was unknown to science until Niko Tinbergen's wife one day noticed gulls digging them up! Although gulls do not dive as well as terns and some other sea birds do, they swim expertly, and a few are able to make brief dives beneath the surface. Experiments at Oxford University have shown that a gull's white breast is not detected and reacted to as quickly by fish, seeing it against a pale sky, as a dark breast; this is an important advantage for gulls, since they cannot pursue fish any distance underwater but must capture them on the first lunge. Some gulls instinctively treat the water, on which they depend, more tenderly than man does; observers in Maryland watched Herring Gulls, which were foraging in streams, fly or swim to land, defecate and then return to their feeding.

We tend to think of gulls as eaters of fish or garbage, a notion that underestimates their adaptability. It was no "miracle" that the California Gulls saved the Mormon's harvest in the last century. In our own time they have been seen cleaning midges from entire meadows, plucking them out of the air or from their resting places on grass and sagebrush. In Utah they devoured mice that were forced by flowing water out of irrigation ditches, becoming, an observer reported, "so perfect in their work that they kept abreast of the head of the water and picked up every mouse that appeared." Clarence Cottam, a well-known naturalist, once wrote an article entitled "Gulls as vegetarians," in which he documented, among other occurrences, California Gulls feeding on sprouting barley in the San Fernando Valley, and Franklin's Gulls in the prairie states feeding "extensively" on wheat, oats and other grains. The Glaucous Gull is known to eat marine algae.

To the gull's success as a fisher, predator and vegetarian can be added its peculiar adeptness as scavenger and pirate. "It is amazing," Tinbergen writes of Holland's canals, "when one tries to look at the canals with a Herring Gull's eyes, to see how well supplied they are." Gulls in Holland find much of their food in canals, patrolling their banks for dead rats, drowned kittens and the other delicacies sloughed off by civilization. Tinbergen also describes the less passive feeding in England of Black-headed Gulls, which haunt the meadows where lapwings capture insects and other small prey; surrounding the lapwings ("like wardens in a Nazi prison camp") they are ready to rush at whatever lapwing catches an insect, and rob the unfortunate bird if it cannot swallow its prize at once. Similar behavior has been described among several species of gulls in Oakland, California, where they have followed large flocks of robins across grassy plots in winter and plundered them of the worms they unearthed.

While gulls themselves are subject to piracy from other species, they have organized their own defenses. One of the most interesting adaptations of this sort apparently occurs among Lava Gulls, a species that breeds and lives out its life in the Galápagos Islands. For a long time it was believed that the bird's uniformly dark plumage and bill (it is also called the Dusky Gull) served as protective coloration. Further study disclosed that it has no enemies in its limited habitat. However, as a scavenger, it gets keen competition along the shore from the larger frigate birds. One ornithologist has come to the conclusion that the color of the gull's plumage blends into that of the lava shoreline where it finds its food, partly concealing it and its feeding from cruising frigate birds.

Such adaptations would not be advantageous for other birds of the same species, which are looking for the same kind of food. We know that Herring Gulls, having sighted food, descend to it in a characteristic figure-eight pattern that attracts other gulls. If the food is plentiful, these gulls utter a "food-finding" call so loud and high-pitched that it carries as far as three miles. Before we comment on the "generosity" of gulls toward their fellows, we might reflect that other kinds of birds also attract their own kind with "food-finding" calls. When food is generally scarce over a region or a season, such behavior may help to preserve the species.

Although gulls share many characteristics, others vary from species to species and even from individual to individual. This variety is one of the fascinations that the world of birds holds for human beings. It is aesthetically pleasing, while the scientific study of avian differences has broadened our knowledge of life itself. But variety among gulls has still further significance. It is, in a sense, the basis for the relationship that has sprung up between gulls and men.

First, let us see what brings about this variety. If our planet were wholly without physical nuances, without different climates and land forms, without bodies of water and marshes

4

and bogs, its living things would look pretty much alike. But all creatures have evolved to take advantage of the different ecological niches that exist in our planet's various habitats. (Ecologists define an organism's habitat as its "address" and its niche as its "profession"—the way in which it gets its living.)

Animals evolve special characteristics that fit them for life on land or in the sea, in caves or in trees, in marshes or in deserts. All unconsciously, each species adapts to fill a niche where it will find the least competition from other species. A hummingbird's long, thin bill allows it to extract nectar from flowers, a heron's long legs and neck allow it to forage in shallow water, a puffin's stubby wings allow it to propel itself underwater in pursuit of small fish.

But environmental conditions change. Mountains rise or are leveled, the climate grows cooler or warmer, the prairie becomes moist or arid. In recent times, man himself has become a "geological force," altering entire habitats. Some creatures adapt to the changes, others do not and either dwindle to remnant populations (whooping cranes, California condors) or become extinct (dinosaurs, saber-toothed tigers).

"Adaptability" is the word we apply to a living thing's capacity to adjust its life to meet changing environmental conditions. A certain number of individuals within a species adapt at first to meet a sudden change in their world. As the successful members of their species, they flourish and pass on their capacity to their descendants, which eventually become dominant. (It was the comparative immunity to DDT of certain individual mosquitoes and house flies that finally produced "resistant" populations.) But it is a continuing story. Within a species a few individuals remain which are not able to adapt to the specific changes as quickly as the others, and these individuals and their descendants do not fare very well. But if the conditions change again within a reasonable time, the second group may flourish and regain dominance. If conditions fluctuate, this variability remains like a reservoir within the species.

Three species: Laughing Gulls (in air), Great Black-backs, Herring Gulls

Thus the Herring Gull, among others, apparently retains variability within its species because the conditions of its world—the advance and withdrawal of glaciers, changing shorelines, and alternating persecution and protection by man—are unstable. At one point, for instance, the members of the Herring Gull population which nested on Maine's outer islands, remote from predatory man, prospered, while those nesting closer to shore usually fell victim to eggers and gunners. In more recent times the inshore nesters have profited by their proximity to dumps and fish canneries, while those on the outer islands, far from this new food supply, produce fewer chicks than they once did.

Adaptation in the evolutionary sense is often misunderstood. An animal does not respond, consciously or unconsciously, to its environment by changing its characteristics as the zebra and the giraffe in Kipling's story acquired stripes and spots in response to the "stripy, speckly, patchy-blotchy shadows" of the forest. As someone has said, evolution is not directive but opportunistic. Living things evolve through accidental changes in their genes (or, as some scientists now believe, in the arrangement of genes), those giant molecules that transmit inheritable characteristics from one generation to another. By controlling the synthesis of enzymes within the body, genes control the structure of the body too. One gene, for instance, may control the size or shape of the wings, another the color of the eyes. Sudden changes in the genes occur at random, caused perhaps by radiation or some other external factor, and these changes are called mutations.

If a mutation occurs within a bird's genetic material, it will alter the characteristic controlled by the affected gene. It may produce some variation in the bird's coloring or the shape of its bill or the length of its wing. Most mutations come to nothing, and indeed may be positively harmful, modifying a characteristic that until then has allowed the bird to function at its best in a hostile environment; a mutation, for instance, that alters the protective coloration of a bird's chicks may leave them more vulnerable to predators. The affected gene is likely to die out with the individual, so the change never becomes incorporated into the genetic material of the species.

But once in a great while such a random change is helpful: a darkening or lightening of the plumage increases the chance that a bird will be undetected by its predator or its prey; a slight enlargement of the bill enables it to exploit a source of food previously untapped by itself or any of its competitors. That bird and the offspring to which it passes its altered genes acquire a certain advantage over others of their kind. The new strain thrives and increases, while the unchanged "weaker" members of the species tend to become scarce or die out altogether. The mutation, occurring by chance originally in a single individual, ultimately strengthens the entire species. This is the real meaning of the expression "the survival of the fittest."

Gulls, like other successful groups, display a wide range of traits and structures stemming from adaptations to many environments. One of the most successful European species is the Black-headed Gull. Like so many names of birds (the purple finch, which is raspberry-colored; the northern water thrush, which is a wood warbler), Black-headed Gull is a misnomer. Its head is chocolate-brown. Although it shares with many other gulls a penchant for garbage, it often follows the plow in the British Isles, seizing the insects stirred up in fields by farm machinery. At dusk it may be seen hawking moths. An even more unusual habit is its method of procuring marine worms; it paddles on the mud or wet sand to set off vibrations, which apparently lure its prey to the surface.

At sea the Black-headed Gull retains its skill, catching fish by plunge-diving, a technique in which it drops quickly to the water, then immerses its head and breast to capture its prey. A long-range flier, it crosses the ocean with increasing frequency today and is now a regular visitor to the Atlantic coast of the United States.

The Franklin's Gull might be called its New World counterpart. This is the "prairie dove" of the American West, where it haunts farmlands in its persistent search for insects. Herbert K. Job, the clergyman

43

and photographer who wrote several books on natural history early in this century, described the prairie farmer followed by a troop of these handsome birds:

> *Without sign of fear they alight in the furrow close behind him, and with graceful carriage, hurry about to pick up the worms and grubs which the plow has just unearthed. Often have I watched the plowman and his snowy retinue, and it appeals to me as one of the prettiest sights which the wide prairies can afford.*

A scientist who shot several of these gulls and examined their stomachs found fifteen different species of insects in one, and three hundred and twenty-seven dragonfly nymphs in another. The birds nest in the marshes and around the lakes of the northern prairie states and southern Canada. They fly as far south in winter as the coast of Chile, and thus are one of the few gulls to cross the equator.

Many of the larger gulls move long distances in season too. California Gulls breed on inland lakes in the Far West, ranging north to Great Slave Lake in Canada, then spend the winter on the Pacific coast. The Glaucous Gull, called the "Burgomaster" because of its large size and domineering manner, often breeds north of the Arctic Circle but is lured far to the south in winter by the prospect of easier meals. "Like the Iceland Gull it frequents open beaches," writes John Bull in *Birds of the New York Area,* "but is especially partial to garbage dumps, where the largest numbers are seen."

Other species live more restricted lives. The Audouin's Gull is apparently one of the least successful of the subfamily; its numbers are now estimated at little more than a thousand pairs and its breeding has become restricted to a few islands in the Mediterranean Sea. As those islands come under greater pressure for development, the Audouin's may become one of the few endangered species among gulls. The Galápagos

Islands, which provide most of the Lava Gull's range, also serve as the breeding grounds of another fairly restricted species, the Swallow-tailed Gull, which may be found at other times of the year along the coast of Peru or in the Bay of Panama. The Swallow-tailed is one of the strangest of all gulls—and, indeed, has even been suspected of being a tern!

Very little was known about this gull until the fall of 1962, when Jack P. Hailman of Duke University visited the Galápagos. A half-century before, an ornithologist, puzzled because he had never seen this gull feeding, had suggested that it might gather its food at night. This remark had been forgotten during the intervening years until Hailman pitched his tent in a sea-lion colony (the only level terrain available), with a clear view of the cliffs on South Plazas Island where Swallow-tailed Gulls nested.

Hailman learned that these gulls, whose tail, incidentally, resembles that of a tern, go through a courting ceremony in which their upright postures are closer to those of terns than of gulls. A close relationship was indicated. Faced by a shortage of vegetation on the small volcanic island, the gulls fashioned their nests of lava stones, coral and sometimes even the spines of sea urchins. In their nests they deposited a single egg.

During the day the adult gulls slept or preened. The chick, when it hatched on the narrow ledge, tended to stay in or very near the nest, for to wander might have been fatal. As dusk approached, Hailman dragged his sleeping bag closer to the cliff's edge, set his alarm so that he would waken periodically and settled down for the night.

At dusk the gulls began to fly out to sea, leaving their mates to brood the chicks. The nights were clear and moonlit and Hailman was able to watch everything that took place. The foraging gulls returned after midnight to relieve their mates, who flew out to sea. Then the feeding process began. The returning adult brought back a squid, which it had swallowed and partly digested, as most gulls do when they bring food back to the nest. But this species has made adaptations unique among gulls. Apparently the Swallow-tailed Gull is equipped with night vision. The eye of the adult is extremely large, like the eye of owls and some other nocturnal creatures. When Hailman shone a flashlight into the adult's eye it reflected the light brightly, a phenomenon he could not produce among the more "normal" gulls he had studied in the United States.

> *Typical of nocturnal animals, this trait lengthens the exposure of the retina to a dimly lit object* [Hailman wrote in Audubon *magazine*]. *Eyeshine usually indicates that the eye has a special structure which reflects, rather than absorbs, light behind the retina. Dissection of several eyes of Swallow-tailed Gull specimens gathered for museum study did show an unusual, blue scaly material along the back of the eye, similar to that found in owls and other night-flying birds.*

Although the chicks of other gulls usually wear dusky plumage for camouflage, the Swallow-tailed Gull chick has a white head, clearly visible in the dark. The chick pecks at the adult's bill, which has white feathers at its base and a white tip, and this action stimulates the adult to regurgitate the meal. The mate returns at dawn, just before patrolling and piratical frigate birds appear, and feeds the chick once more.

Hailman established the fact that the Swallow-tailed is the only nocturnal gull. What caused this bird to deviate from the habits of other gull species? Hailman put forward two speculations. The first was that there is a great deal of competition among sea birds in the area—other gulls, shearwaters, albatrosses and boobies. A source of food that was not being exploited was squid, which comes to the surface at night. A bird that could exploit that ecological niche would have a copious source of food all to itself, which is this gull's enviable position today. A further stimulation to nocturnal feeding, Hailman believed, was the presence of the piratical frigate birds around the island during the day.

For those of us who delight in the abundance of echoic patterns and mirror images in nature, Jack Hailman's descriptions of the

Herring Gull eggs

Swallow-tailed Gull are especially enlightening. That gull, restricted to the equatorial Galápagos Islands, has a wide-ranging counterpart far to the north. Evolving independently, the Black-legged Kittiwake also took to the cliffs during the nesting season and made similar adaptations to this special and somewhat hazardous environment.

The attractive little Kittiwake is not a rare bird. Although the most pelagic, or ocean-going, of gulls, it is a familiar sight to many observers around Great Britain and off both the Atlantic and Pacific shores of Canada and the United States. On one December day in 1973, William C. Townsend, a high school teacher and an excellent "birder," counted 10,052 Kittiwakes off Eastport, Maine (and estimated that he missed about four thousand more).

Kittiwakes (their name is imitative of their cry) are white-headed, white-bodied gulls with gray wings, the tips of which look "dipped in ink." They feed on marine organisms and small fish such as capelins and lance fish, either landing on the water and thrusting the head beneath the surface to seize their prey or diving headlong from the air and pursuing fish to depths of five or six feet. Using their long wings as fins, they are the only gulls that swim underwater. Kittiwakes are so well adapted to oceanic life that a naturalist who kept one captive later wrote that it "refused fresh water and drank salt water eagerly."

Yet like all other thriving sea birds, the Kittiwake has also adapted to those few traumatic months when it must come ashore to breed. Like the Swallow-tailed Gull, it nests on cliffs, but on cliffs in the northern seas. The steepness of these refuges and the narrow nesting ledges (sometimes only four inches wide) discourage predators but present the parent birds with other problems in carrying out the most routine movements. Fierce winds eddying about a cliff face may turn an approach or a landing into a hazardous undertaking. Even copulation must be managed with great care. Among most species of gulls, copulation takes place with the female standing, the male mounting her back rather uneasily; finally, as the act is completed and she moves away, her mate ingloriously loses his balance and falls off. On a four-inch ledge, whipped by turbulent winds, a species that carried on in such a fashion might soon create a surplus of neurotic males; the female Kittiwake accommodates her mate by assuming a sitting position.

A. C. Bent has given us one of the first human-eye views of the Kittiwake's precarious nesting sites and of the intrepid naturalists who have studied them. In 1904 he visited Bird Rocks in the Gulf of St. Lawrence, where a large colony nested. He arrived at night, approaching the island in a small boat in lively seas:

> *As the great cliffs towered above us in the moonlight we saw a lantern coming down the ladder to show us where to land and we ran in among the breakers. There was a crash which brought us to our feet as we struck an unseen rock; but the next wave carried us over it and landed us among the rocks and flying spray. We were overboard in an instant, struggling in the surf up to our waists, for the boat was rapidly filling, as wave after wave broke over us. A few moments of rapid work served to unload our baggage and attach a stout line to the boat, the signal was passed aloft and the powerful steam winch above landed her high and dry. After exchanging hearty greetings with our genial host, Captain Bourque, we enjoyed the novel experience of being hoisted up in a crate to the top of the cliff, over 100 feet high. It was certainly a new and interesting sensation to feel ourselves slowly rising in the darkness up the face of those somber cliffs, with the surf thundering on the rocks below us and with a cloud of screaming seabirds hovering about us, barely discernible in the moonlight, like a swarm of ghostly bats whose slumber had been disturbed and who were protesting at our rude intrusion.*

The next day Bent was lowered, squatting in the crate at the end of a long rope, down the perpendicular face of the cliff. There, suspended and sometimes whirling dizzily in the wind only a few feet from the nesting shelves, he was able to photograph "the gentle, confiding birds" at whatever leisure he was able to muster. And some people sneer at the tame pastime of bird watching!

Ornithologists continue to uncover new facts about this remarkable bird and its ability to maintain its numbers in a harsh environment. The biologist Esther Cullen has studied Kittiwakes off the British Isles and further documented their adaptations to cliff-nesting. Apparently they often delay the building of their nests until after heavy rains, when the necessary mud becomes available. Kittiwakes are so accustomed to life at sea that they are reluctant to make the necessary flights over land to collect mud, grass and other nesting materials. They seem to prefer to collect them in the company of their colleagues, so that often dozens of these gulls fly off together and return to the cliffs carrying beakfuls of the stuff. Even more to their taste is a little nonviolent thievery. They will often wait for a neighbor to leave its nest, then filch its nesting material. The thievery goes on, Cullen writes, "to such an extent that half- or almost-finished nests may be dismantled completely."

In any case, Kittiwakes usually take much longer at their nest-building than other gulls. The shallow, loosely fashioned nests which gulls build on the ground will not do on the windy, treacherous cliffs. The Kittiwake returns to its ledge carrying nesting material, collected honestly or not, in its long yellow bill. First it brings mud, dropping it on the ledge and trampling it to form a solid base for the nest. Then it builds up high walls of mud, grass and seaweeds, and lines the resultant deep inner cup with soft grasses. Thus it builds a sort of crib, restraining wobbly eggs or restless chicks. While most gulls lay three eggs as a hedge against predation by their own or other species, Kittiwakes lay only two, one of which usually fails to hatch; predators are less of a menace than overcrowding on the narrow ledges. (It will be remembered that the Swallow-tailed Gull, also a cliff-nester, lays but one egg.)

Kittiwakes keep right on behaving in their own fashion after the chicks hatch. Most gulls remove the empty eggshells and the chicks' droppings from the nest because they are likely to catch the eye of a predator flying overhead; Kittiwakes don't bother. Studies on many gulls have shown that while they cannot recognize their own eggs when they have been removed from the nest, they are able to distinguish their own chicks from others after a few days. Kittiwakes are unable to recognize their own chicks for several weeks. After all, as Cullen remarks, Kittiwake chicks are like Kittiwake eggs—they are not likely to stray from the nest, and there is no need for their parents to learn to recognize them. It is sufficient to know the right nest.

Many adult gulls have bright-red bills or bright contrasting markings on their bills at which the chicks lunge and peck to stimulate the parent to disgorge the food it has brought. The Kittiwake's bill is uniformly yellow and thus does not lure the chick into lunging in a place where a slight miscalculation might end in disaster. Instead, the parent lands on the nest and opens its bill, which is lined in a bright orange-red and serves as a prominent target. The chick takes the food directly from the parent's throat.

Like the Swallow-tailed Gull's chick, the Kittiwake's is not camouflaged; its plumage is white with dusky tips. It, too, has adapted to survive not so much in a world of enemies, but in a place where it might be its own worst enemy. Chicks of many other species exercise their flight muscles and practice "flying" by flapping their wings in the nest, almost invariably turning to face into the wind. Kittiwakes practice too, but they always turn and face the cliff wall. Then, when that startling moment finally arrives and the chick is able to lift itself off the nest by its own wing power, the young bird does not find itself hanging hundreds of feet above the abyss. (Herring Gulls usually nest on lower ground, but when they choose cliffs their chicks do not display these adaptations.)

In an environment not yet overrun by technological man, the Swallow-tailed Gull of the Galápagos Islands has used its adaptive skills only to deal with natural phenomena. The Black-legged Kittiwake, however, lives in a different world. For years Kittiwakes have supplemented their winter food supply by shadowing the offshore fishing fleets and now, following the lead of other northern gulls, they are adapting to man-made environments. From the British Isles come reports that in some cases Kittiwakes have abandoned the seafaring life to forage for scraps along polluted rivers. Losing their fear of land, these inveterate cliff-nesters have taken to building their nests on the narrow window ledges of old buildings in Scotland.

It is during the breeding season that gulls, like other animals, seem most "alive"—their senses and responses are pitched to the keenest edge and they unfold themselves to observers in all their beauty and diversity. Some of our most profound knowledge about the drives and stratagems of animals has been gathered by the men and women who study the breeding behavior of our familiar gulls. And yet this is the point at which even the hardiest and most adaptable animals are vulnerable. The adult gulls, generally restricted to the vicinity of the nest, are often exposed to predators, human or

5

otherwise. Their helpless chicks, even under the best of care, must rely on a unique combination of instinctive and learned behavior to see them through the early weeks of their lives. On the success of both parents and chicks in coming to grips with the special problems of this period may depend the future of the species.

One of the most helpful characteristics these birds display, as far as their observers are concerned, is what biologists call by the German word *ortstreue,* "place faithfulness." The adult birds tend to return to the same nesting site year after year, drawn there, as Maeterlinck said of his bees, "as though space had preciously preserved the indelible track of their flight." The larger gulls, such as the Herring Gull, are usually not ready to breed until their fifth summer of life. By then the drab brownish garb of the juvenile bird has matured through a succession of molts to the sparkling nuptial plumage the adult acquires in its fourth winter.

Niko Tinbergen, who moved from Holland to Oxford after World War II, was the first observer to document step by step the intricate signals and rituals that gulls have evolved through the ages to stake out their individual nesting territories, choose the right mate, produce their young, and nourish and defend them during the critical weeks when they are growing toward self-sufficiency. From his blind, or hide, on shores and islands off the coast of northern Europe, Tinbergen spent many hours a day watching the birds and puzzling out what their seemingly chaotic and random movements meant. ("It is amazing how much one can detect, when one looks or takes photographs, against the light while the sun is still low," he writes in *The Animal in Its World,* providing one of the most compelling reasons yet for becoming an early riser.)

He saw the males fight to define and defend their territories, using their bills and flailing wings to deal painful blows to their opponents. He saw, too, that each gull's response to an encounter with a rival was a curious mixture of aggression and fear, of the fierce urge to charge and a heartfelt desire to turn tail; posturing is so much less painful than violence. The postures that are the essence of most encounters between fire-breathing males, Tinbergen saw, are really signals. One gull advances on another with its neck stretched upward and its bill pointing down, its wings pushed slightly forward. Bill and wings are its weapons, and the gull brandishes them like fists.

Tinbergen also deciphered the calls and postures of sex. He described the male's "long calls" that coax the female in to share his territory, and the ensuing ambivalent behavior when the female responds. Primed to defend his arduously won territory against all comers, the male is torn between courtly and aggressive approaches when the female at last descends to him. The female, too, is on her guard, and the outcome of the encounter, Tinbergen saw, depends upon her attitude. Wary of any threatening behavior on her part, the male is poised, ready to charge. But the responsive female assumes the "appeasement" posture, body hunched with neck drawn in, wings held close to her sides, frequently turning her bill away to indicate that there is no menace in it.

When the male is sufficiently mollified, the female approaches him, uttering her soft "begging" call. She pecks gently at the base of his bill. This, Tinbergen remarks, is "cupboard love," for she is asking to be fed. The male responds to her calls and pecks, as both of them later will to the advances of their chicks—by regurgitating a mass of partly digested food. The female eagerly consumes it and the bond between them grows more secure. The male continues to feed the female periodically during subsequent days. This act is in part symbolic, cementing the bonds, but it is also utilitarian in that the female takes added nourishment at a time when her eggs are developing.

As gulls stimulate others on the nesting grounds, so Tinbergen stimulated a generation of biologists to get out on the beaches and islands and record the intricate behavior and relationships of mating sea birds. There is still a great deal we do not know. But every year the scientific journals fatten themselves on the facts and figures compiled and analyzed by all of those biologists who sit patiently in blinds, or set up field experiments, and add to our knowledge of these fascinating beings.

We know now that even sex among gulls is not a predictable and mechanistic procedure. Under the stress of overcrowding in some colonies, male Herring and Lesser Black-backed Gulls (originally described as "monogamous") are regularly observed in the act of wandering into nearby territories and attempting to court and mount their neighbors' mates. Sex is merely functional among animals, we are sometimes told; but Black-headed Gulls go right on copulating after their eggs have hatched. Mounting his mate, flapping his wings vigorously and uttering a loud, deep note in his ecstasy, the male gull indulges himself in what Vladimir Nabokov has called "that routine rhythm which shakes the world."

But facts and figures, not ecstasy, are what we are pursuing here, and they come in an avalanche during the nesting season. Male and female gulls work together to weave their nests. All available materials— grass, twigs, seaweeds, soil, hanks of twine—go into them. (That most ferocious of gulls, the Great Black-backed, sometimes slips the dried carcass of one of its victims—perhaps a small bird—into the fabric.) Three is the usual clutch of eggs. The Herring Gull, we are told by several observers, lays three eggs ninety percent of the time.

If a fourth egg is laid, the brooding gull may not be able to cover it, and it is likely to cool fatally or be snatched by a predator. In fact, if a fourth egg is found on a nest, it is often of a different size and color than the others and may have been deposited there by another, perhaps confused, bird. As long as there is at least one egg left in a nest after a disturbance, the gulls will go on brooding it as if nothing had happened. If all are removed or smashed, the female may lay another clutch.

It is well to remember that gulls, though successful, are not superanimals. They are visited by natural disasters like any other living thing, and there is much that can go wrong during the approximately four weeks of incubation or in the first weeks of the chicks' lives. Savage storms may wash away the entire product of a nesting season, impelling

Herring Gulls mating

waves and high tides over low-lying islands, smashing the eggs and leaving the chicks strewn among the flotsam and kelp in the limp grass. Prolonged heavy rains are a frequent hazard for chicks, soaking them to the skin and chilling them fatally. A great storm that battered Gull Island at Witless Bay, Newfoundland, in 1973 killed perhaps ninety percent of the three thousand Herring Gull chicks expected to fledge there that summer. Many of the adults ate their dead young and gave up any further attempt to nest that year. As usual, the strong survived; Great Black-backed Gulls, who had taken the choice nesting places on higher ground for themselves, suffered few losses.

Gulls also pay a heavy toll to predators of their own or other species during the nesting season. Their close relatives, the jaegers (which Bent calls "the notorious pirates and freebooters among sea birds") attack the eggs and chicks of gulls in the far north. Caracaras, long-legged scavengers of the falcon family, have been seen destroying a thirty-six-nest colony of the Brown-hooded Gull in the Argentine marshes. At Ravenglass on the Irish Sea, Tinbergen noted that Black-headed Gulls often cannibalized their neighbors' chicks just after they had hatched. The wet, glistening chicks slipped down the gullet easily, but after a few hours the chicks became dry and fluffy, and a gull that made off with one had a hard time swallowing it (Tinbergen saw a stubborn adult struggle for ten minutes before it was finally able to gulp down its prize). The larger Herring Gulls, however, had no trouble swallowing dry Black-headed Gull chicks.

Gulls, as a rule, do not passively submit to predation at their nests, having evolved a number of protective devices. Some other kinds of birds, such as ducks and pheasants, sit tight on the nest at a potential predator's approach, trusting to their protective coloration to see them through the crisis. The predator is not always fooled. As Dean Amadon writes, "Brooding ducks are often caught by foxes; this is believed to be one reason males outnumber females in some waterfowl." Lacking protective coloration, gulls invariably take to the air whether the predator

Gull eating egg from neighbor gull's unguarded nest

comes by wing or by foot. They trust to their eggs' mottled shells (which are produced by a specialized pigmentation system in the upper oviduct), or to the instinct of their pepper-and-salt-colored chicks to freeze where they are. As a further precaution, many gulls (Kittiwakes, as we have seen, are an exception) remove eggshells from the nest soon after the young have hatched lest their pale, glistening linings attract predators.

In any case, the harassment from scores of screeching, diving adults is likely to unfocus a predator's attention just enough to divert it from carrying out its mission on the heavily camouflaged nests. It is on such occasions that the most vulnerable nests will be those isolated or built on the fringes of the colony, where the harassment is less intense. Here, again, the strongest birds, by winning the desirable nesting sites, are likely to be at the heart of a well-defended area.

But even the strongest gulls do not have things all their own way in man's world. Although Black-headed Gulls in England often nest on dunes, Tinbergen concludes that it is not the best habitat for them. Marauding foxes have killed as many as two hundred and thirty incubating gulls in a single night on the dunes at Ravenglass Sanctuary. Previously these gulls nested on islands in inland lakes where they were safe from foxes, but when the preferred lakes were drained for agriculture and various development schemes, the gulls were forced to find other nesting places. They have not yet hit upon a good defense against foxes.

Once it has hatched, the young gull quickly learns to cope with the problems of survival; slow learners are doomed. Like every other organism, the chick comes into the world provided with certain pre-existing behavior patterns, but it must learn to order them so that it functions as efficiently as possible. Tinbergen was the first to show the significance of the red marks on the bills of adult gulls (such as that of the Herring Gull). He decided that the marks were targets at which chicks peck to stimulate the parent to regurgitate the food it has brought to the nest. The chick, however, apparently doesn't know this at first and its early attempts to feed itself are hit-and-miss. All it has is the pecking motion. By pecking at moving objects around it—the parent's bill or even the bills of its feeding siblings—it finally strikes food by accident.

> *The newly-hatched gull chick begins life with a clumsily-coordinated, poorly aimed peck motivated by simple stimulus properties of shape and movement provided only by a parent or sibling [Jack P. Hailman wrote in* Scientific American]. *It cannot recognize food, but by aiming at the bills of its relatives and missing it strikes food and rapidly learns to recognize it. As a result of the reward embodied in the food, the chick comes to learn the visual characteristics of the parent. Through practice in pecking its aim and depth perception improve steadily.*

Such research and hypothesis carry implications far beyond the remote gulleries where chicks begin their battle for survival. It sheds new light on that "mosaic" of components, learned and instinctive, that directs the behavior of living things.

The individual chick's battle will be against great odds. Studies on Herring Gulls and Ringed-billed Gulls show that while seventy-two percent of their eggs will hatch, only thirty-one percent of the chicks will survive to leave the colony. Storms and predators, disease and accident, the extremes of heat and cold, all take their toll; as the fogs of late spring dissolve under the burning sun of midsummer, the growing chicks begin to wander in search of shade, and returning to the nest, cross strange territories where edgy adults, primed to repel intruders, often attack and mangle them.

The attrition does not end with fledging. Once the chicks leave the nesting colony they are on their own, abandoned in most cases by their parents to feed and care for themselves. The primary niche many kinds of gulls have evolved for themselves through the ages is as scavengers along the world's shorelines. Here they are free from competition by

61

more specialized feeders. Some years ago the ornithologists E. H. Forbush and J. B. May wrote of the traditional view of the large gulls, feeding on "much filthy, floating refuse that might otherwise be cast back by winds and tides on beach and shore. Whenever fish killed in thousands by disease, frost or other causes, are cast up in countless multitudes upon the shore to poison the air with the offensive effluvia of decay, there the gulls gather and in an astonishingly short time succeed in abating the nuisance."

But under normal conditions many juvenile gulls get less than their share of nature's bounty. The adults retreat from the nesting colonies to their winter feeding territories along the shore, which they often defend against other gulls, juveniles as well as adults. Starvation is a real threat to the young scavengers during those harsh early months.

How is it, then, with this severe natural mortality which keeps most organisms "in balance" with their environment, that several kinds of gulls have increased their numbers so spectacularly in this century? Man, of course, is the great dislocating force. Just as his manipulations in agriculture and forestry have converted into "pests" many insects that were previously held in check by natural forces, so he has given a large percentage of juvenile gulls the means to stave off disaster. Gulls, highly mobile, sharp-eyed scavengers to begin with, are ideally equipped to take advantage of the variety of refuse that man has made available to them.

Sudden change, for good or ill, is a part of the gulls' background and they are equipped to deal with that too.

It is hard for us to believe today that naturalists once feared for the survival of many species of gulls along the coasts of North America. When someone speaks of endangered species we tend to think of whooping cranes or bald eagles, or perhaps of Eskimo curlews, those plump, long-billed shore birds which once migrated in flocks of thousands, were slaughtered the same way and are now on the edge of extinction. Gulls flourish along our coasts and even inland in numbers that must satisfy their most ardent admirers. And so we have to go back to a time when these graceful birds

6

aroused a meaner form of admiration and clung to existence by no very certain tenure.

The bad years for gulls and for a great many other wild things in North America came during the final decades of the nineteenth century. That was the "age of extermination." The bison herds were decimated by a generation of Buffalo Bills, shot from horseback as part of the genocide compaign against the Indians, and even, "just for fun," from the windows of railroad cars; their bleached bones could be seen piled along the tracks of the Santa Fe Railroad in a vast pile, twelve feet high and a half-mile long, awaiting shipment to fertilizer plants in the East. "Nowhere," wrote Horace Greeley, "is the blind, senseless human appetite for carnage, for destruction, more strikingly, more lamentably evinced than in the rapidly proceeding extermination of the buffalo." The same mentality that ravaged American forests with saw and fire soon shot the passenger pigeon and the heath hen to extinction.

But in general the birds suffering most were those whose nature kept them close to the water during the breeding season or on migration. The first North American bird to disappear after the arrival of the Europeans was the great auk, a large, flightless sea bird closely related to the puffins and guillemots. This was the bird originally called "penguin" by the Portuguese fishermen, a word only later applied to the totally unrelated flightless birds of the Antarctic. The great auk was doomed as soon as the fishermen began going ashore on its nesting islands in the North Atlantic. It was easily killed with sticks, then salted away in barrels to be used on long voyages as food or bait. Whole colonies, so the story goes, were sometimes marched across planks like little regiments, onto ships where the crewmen could more conveniently kill and preserve them. The last great auk was bludgeoned to death by fishermen on the volcanic island of Eldey, off Iceland, in 1844.

Shore birds, a large and diverse group which includes the plovers and sandpipers, were threatened en masse. Most of these birds nest in the far north among the grasses, icy pools and briefly blooming wild flowers of the tundra. On the way to or from the tundra they traverse the thousands of miles connecting it with their winter homes, which may be anywhere from the Gulf Coast of the United States to Mexico and South America. Under the best of circumstances during the last century the shore birds were forced twice each year to run the gauntlet of guns held by those who were out for sport or for food.

Soon shore-bird hunting became big business. Market gunners scoured the coast for these birds, selling the ones they shot to restaurants, hotels or wholesalers. An economy of scale was at work here. The shore birds fly in large flocks, and at high tide crowd together on rocks and beaches, giving the impression from a little distance of some tightly massed vegetation. A gunner was able to kill dozens of the smaller birds with a single "blaze at the feathers."

A lighthouse keeper, describing the hunting of small sandpipers, or "peeps," on an island off the coast of Maine, wrote: "They form in flocks and sit on the shore. Gunners come here and slaughter them awfully, for it is no trick to fire into a big flock of them and wound a large number. After the gunners have been here, my children bring in many wounded ones, some with broken wings or legs shot off, or eyes shot out, in all shapes. The gunners don't get half they shoot down."

And in 1948 Ralph S. Palmer, writing in *Maine Birds* about one of the larger sandpipers, the lesser yellowlegs, gave some indication of the market gunners' impact: "This bird has not yet recovered from the heavy shooting which lasted five decades. Data from shooting journals of Scarborough hunters show that this species was much hunted in August. From 1842 to 1845 [Caleb G.] Loring shot 4093 . . . In the early 1880s, the Parker House and other Boston hotels paid gunners 50 cents per bird for Lesser Yellowlegs."

Many species of shore birds, among them the golden plover and the Hudsonian godwit, were greatly reduced in numbers, though only the Eskimo curlew apparently passed the point of no return before laws stopped the carnage. But there was yet another use to which man put birds, which further added to the almost intolerable pressure on their harassed populations. This use might be summed up in the word "fashion." Medieval crusaders, Renaissance dandies and native American chieftains adorned their heads or headgear with plumes of differing shapes and colors; "panache" is a word derived from the Latin for feather, *pinna*, and is suggestive of the dash and swagger we associate with such ornament.

For hundreds of years the acquisitiveness stimulated in man by the sight of splendid plumage caused few problems for wild birds. Many of the feathers were taken from barnyard fowl, including the most gorgeous of all, the peacock. The Mayas prized the quetzal for its long green plumes which, like the source of the peacock's pride, are not true tail feathers, but upper tail coverts. The Mayas did not kill quetzals for their plumage; fortunately for this wild tropical species, it belongs to an order of birds called Trogons, from whose thin, tender skins (described by one ornithologist as the "flimsiest imaginable excuse for an epidermis") the feathers tear away at a touch. The Mayas, practicing the concept of sustained yield, simply relieved the quetzals of their long plumes and turned them loose to grow another set.

But in the last part of the nineteenth century a passion flared up among American and western European women to adorn themselves with the plumage of birds. The student can pinpoint the date almost exactly, for it was in 1875 that *Godey's Lady's Book* began to feature the plumed look for women of fashion. As Robert Henry Welker points out in his excellent book, *Birds and Men,* the plumage fad was not an isolated phenomenon but one flamboyant stroke among many that created what came to be called the "Gilded Age." Hats, coiffures and derrières, like furniture and "cottages," grew massive, and in the eyes of many later commentators, vulgar and ostentatious. Ornateness became the criterion of the desirable. Milliners, detecting a good thing, aggressively pushed the new fashions. Soon plumes and even whole birds adorned the hair, hats and gowns of the well-dressed woman. Ostriches

Razorbills, close relatives of the extinct great auk

(whose plumes may be clipped without harm to the birds) were imported from Africa and raised on "ostrich ranches" in the western United States in the 1880s. But for the most part the plumes used by milliners were taken from wild birds shot solely for that purpose.

The public's demand for the plumage of wild birds became almost insatiable. Women attended social functions in gowns looped with blackbirds, or shopped and strolled under hats that bristled with egrets' plumes. A typical nineteenth-century social note observed that "Miss — looked extremely well in white, with a whole nest of sparkling, scintillating birds in her hair, which it would have puzzled an ornithologist to classify."

It is true that only an ornithologist of formidable learning was able to appreciate the variety to be found among the milliners' creations. On two strolls through Manhattan's shopping districts in 1896, Frank M. Chapman of the American Museum of Natural History counted, with a bird watcher's zeal, seven hundred hats, five hundred and forty-two of which were decorated with plumage of some kind. He recognized forty different species, including Wilson's warblers, pileated woodpeckers, Acadian owls, bluebirds, pine grosbeaks and a northern shrike, or "butcherbird." Most of the unadorned hats, Chapman noted, belonged to "ladies in mourning or elderly ladies."

Some shore birds were shot for the millinery trade, especially the long-billed species which, when their prepared heads were mounted among a decorative *nature mort* on a woman's head, added a bizarre touch. But their drab rock-and-sand grays and browns were not in much demand. And among the more flamboyant colors, the pinks and carmines of, for instance, the roseate spoonbills tended to fade rather quickly. White remained fashion's preference. The birds most sought after by the millinery gunners became the *Ardeidae*, or long-legged waders, which include the herons and egrets, and the *Laridae*, or gulls and terns.

Gulls, though common along the Atlantic coast earlier in the nineteenth century, were already somewhat reduced in numbers by the time the great millinery slaughter began. The English settlers had brought from the old country a taste for gulls and their eggs. Gulls were often part of the fare at banquets in the big houses of England, and during the seventeenth century the chicks were collected on their breeding grounds and fattened in gull houses on country estates. Noble ladies sent gulls as gifts for the tables of neighboring houses, just as later generations might send a ham or a brace of pheasants.

7

Black-headed Gulls seem to have been especially prized. H. Kruuk, an ornithologist who studied these gulls in England, often came across them, freshly killed in their colonies by foxes. He and his adventurous colleagues gathered the dead gulls and ate them. Recently he wrote that they proved to be "very good fare indeed. It is not clear why the black-headed gull is no longer appreciated as a game-bird."

Kittiwakes were killed by New England fishermen in large numbers for food and bait well into the twentieth century. The little gulls were lured to boats by cod livers and other morsels tossed over the side. "They are tame and unsuspicious, gathering, like terns, in large flocks over a fallen companion, making it easy for the gunner to kill as many as he chooses," a naturalist wrote. In England they were slaughtered on their nesting grounds, though they were protected until July; since Kittiwakes nest comparatively late, the young had not come off the nest when the closed season expired. A nineteenth-century British writer described the result:

> Parties are formed on our eastern coast for the sole purpose of shooting them; and I have seen a person station himself at the top of a kittiwake cliff on the Isle of May, and shoot incessantly for several hours, without so much as afterward picking up a single individual of the many killed and maimed birds with which the smooth water was strewn beneath.

Gulls' eggs remained an important source of food for many coastal people even longer. I have eaten them scrambled and as an ingredient in cakes, and will vouch for their pleasant taste, which has a hint of the sea in it. Tinbergen recalls his egging expeditions, "culminating in boiling or frying the eggs on a little fire of driftwood on the beach or, better still, scrambling them raw with some brandy or sugar." It is true that modern diners may be put off at first by the yolk's uncompromising orange (which acquires a pinkish cast when they are scrambled), but I have seen people equally startled by the rich yellow yolks of fresh "barnyard" eggs, so different from the pallid supermarket variety to which they have grown accustomed.

In any event, gulls' eggs were not only tasty for many of our ancestors but free for the taking. A colony in Norfolk, England, according to Kruuk, has an annual yield even today of thirty thousand eggs. Such colonies produce a sustained yield under careful regulation. There was no regulation at all in American bird colonies a century ago. The Ring-billed Gull, which, according to Audubon and other early naturalists, once commonly nested on the East Coast of the United States and Canada, was apparently driven by eggers to remote nesting grounds inland. The Great Black-backed Gull also disappeared as a breeding bird from the Maine coast. Eggers seriously reduced the nesting population of Western Gulls on the Farallon Islands off San Francisco. (Elsewhere, however, these gulls took advantage of the eggers' presence, following them when they invaded colonies of murres and other sea birds and eating eggs in the nests of birds which had flown away at the men's approach.)

The collection of gulls' eggs (or those of any other sea bird) was generally carried out in two steps. The eggers customarily rowed to the nesting islands and smashed all of the eggs in the area over which they planned to collect. A few days later, assured that the eggs they found would be freshly laid, they returned to collect them, packed them in barrels and took them back to the mainland. They kept some for themselves and sold the rest. Gulls usually re-lay after all of their eggs are taken or destroyed, but modern studies show that chicks hatching later in the season have much poorer chances of survival than those which hatch early in summer; often the parents' drive to care for them wanes with the summer, or cold weather arrives before the chicks have learned to fend for themselves.

The adaptable Herring Gulls, which withstood the raids of the eggers much better than other species by retreating to the outer islands, were suddenly attacked by the millinery gunners around 1875. This

71

added blow was almost too much for them. At that time they seldom nested south of Penobscot Bay on the Maine coast, though they straggled farther south in winter. Gunners (in many cases the same men doubled as eggers or pot hunters) regularly visited the breeding islands to shoot the adults for their plumage; being large and white, gulls' feathers and even their wings were especially popular for the decoration of women's hats. Late in the nineteenth century, as gulls became increasingly scarce, dealers paid forty cents apiece for adults and twenty cents for the brown immature birds. In 1899 a New York millinery dealer furnished eastern Maine's Passamaquoddy Indians with guns and ammunition to kill gulls of all kinds.

The hardy Herring Gull declined all along the coast, even in those regions to the south where nonbreeding birds had once been common. Edward Sturtevant, an ornithologist in Rhode Island, reported that he did not see a Herring Gull there for four summers during the 1870s. William H. Drury has pointed out that in a series of photographs of the shores of Cape Cod and the Provincetown fishing fleet taken at the turn of the century, not a single gull was visible in the background. Only the strain of gulls that had taken to nesting on the outermost islands survived in any numbers. The ornithologist E. H. Forbush ventured the opinion that as "summer people" spread to the islands they would ensure the gulls' extirpation from the entire region.

A reaction finally set in against the slaughter. It surfaced first among a small group of professionals who had become concerned about the future of American birds. In 1883 three naturalists, all of whom were identified with New England, wrote to a number of their colleagues proposing the creation of an organization to promote the "advancement of American ornithology." The three men who conceived the idea for an American Ornithologists' Union (AOU) were Joel A. Allen and William Brewster of Harvard and Elliott Coues, a native of New Hampshire who was teaching at the time at Columbian (later George Washington) University in Washington.

Herring Gull preening

Allen, a man of impressive whiskers and learning, was America's most respected mammalogist as well as a student of birds. Brewster was the foremost field ornithologist of his time; in an era when satisfactory guidebooks and optical aids did not exist, his skill at ferreting out nests and identifying distant birds by form or note was remarkable. Coues, a former U.S. Army surgeon, wrote a number of accurate, sometimes acerbic books about birds for the federal government; and his interests ranged beyond birds to such matters as psychical research and theosophy, though he was ejected from the latter movement for "heresy." Other ornithologists heeded the call, and the AOU held its first meeting at the American Museum of Natural History in 1883.

While the AOU promoted the study of ornithology in this country, it also helped to preserve the creatures its members proposed to study. Its Bird Protection Committee assembled reports on the status of various birds, concluding that at least five million were killed every year for the millinery trade. Its individual members often took an active interest in local bird protection, and later on, several of them increased the scope of their protection work by cooperating with other groups outside the confines of an organization primarily devoted to scientific study.

But that was in the future. Meanwhile, there was a colorful but abortive attempt to involve the layman in bird protection. It originated, as so much early conservation activity did, among circles whose chief purpose was to conserve enough wildlife to shoot. The founder of the first Audubon Society was George Bird Grinnell, editor of the famous sportsmen's magazine *Forest and Stream.* Grinnell, although he was a slightly built, scholarly man, had had a great deal of experience in the outdoors. He collected fossil vertebrates in the West with the influential paleontologist O. C. Marsh. He explored the Black Hills with General George Custer. He lived with the Pawnee Indians, taking part in their hunts and ceremonies. Later he was to help found, with Theodore Roosevelt and other well-to-do big-game hunters, the Boone and Crockett Club in New York.

But in the middle 1880s his thoughts turned increasingly to the unregulated killing of American wildlife. In his editorials in *Forest and Stream* he attacked the practice of hunting wild game for the market and urged restraint by sportsmen. In 1886 he widened his aim to include the protection of birds that were not normally killed for food or sport. As a boy, Grinnell had lived on the estate left by John James Audubon to his family in New York City, and he attended a school that Audubon's widow, Lucy, conducted for small children. He spent much of his boyhood in and around the Audubon home, surrounded by mementoes of the great painter of American birds. To Audubon he later traced his early interest in the natural world.

On February 11, 1886, Grinnell wrote an editorial for his magazine in which he suggested a novel method of abating the indiscriminate killing:

> *We propose the formation of an Association for the protection of wild birds and their eggs, which shall be called the Audubon Society. Its membership is to be free to everyone who is willing to lend a helping hand in forwarding the objects for which it is formed. These objects will be to prevent, so far as possible, (1) the killing of any wild birds not used for food; (2) the destruction of nests or eggs of any wild bird; and (3) the wearing of feathers as ornaments or trimming for dress.*

Grinnell had his target firmly in mind. While he had always recognized the part played in the destruction of American birds by greedy sportsmen and professional gunners, he also saw other potent forces that had largely escaped attention: the women whose tastes stimulated the killing of egrets, gulls and other beautiful birds, and mischievous children who hunted songbirds with small arms and slingshots or smashed their nests and eggs. The Audubon Society was aimed chiefly at them, although anyone could join. *Forest and Stream* supported the society, requiring only that its members uphold its "objects."

The response was overwhelming. Within a little over a year nearly thirty-nine thousand men, women and children signed pledges and acquired memberships. The Audubon Society incorporated in the state of New York, listing a distinguished group of incorporators. Among the society's new members were such notables as Oliver Wendell Holmes and Henry Ward Beecher. Charles Dudley Warner, who had collaborated with Mark Twain on the novel *The Gilded Age*, congratulated Grinnell for founding the society, adding, "A dead bird does not help the appearance of an ugly woman, and a pretty woman needs no such adornment." Not quite so pithy were the remarks of the society's most revered member, John Greenleaf Whittier, who wrote only three days after Grinnell's editorial was published:

> *I heartily approve of the proposed Audubon Society. We are in a way to destroy both our forests and our birds. A society for the preservation of the latter has long been needed, and I hope it is not too late for the accomplishment of its objects. I could almost wish that the shooters of the birds, the taxidermists who prepare their skins, and the fashionable wearers of their feathers might share the penalty which was visited upon the Ancient Mariner who shot the Albatross.*

But the financial burden and the general apathy outside the pale of the society itself finally proved to be too great a burden for *Forest and Stream*. At the end of 1888 the first Audubon Society expired, not without a parting blast from Grinnell:

> *Essays have been written to demonstrate the foolishness of small bird destruction, laws have been passed to protect the useful species, societies have been organized and tens of thousands of members enrolled pledged against the fatuous fashion of wearing bird skins as dress; arguments, pleas, appeals to reason and appeals to sentiment have been urged; and what is the outcome of it all? Fashion decrees feathers; and feathers*

Typical Gull nesting island

it is. The headgear of women is made up in as large a degree as ever be-
fore of the various parts of small birds. Thousands and millions of birds
are displayed in every conceivable shape on the hats and bonnets. This
condition of affairs must be something of a shock to the leaders of the
Audubon Society, who were sanguine enough to believe that the moral
idea represented by their movement would be efficacious to influence soci-
ety at large.

Nevertheless, the sentiment that had inspired the Audubon Society
lived on. In England, where W. H. Hudson and other writers helped to
create sympathetic attitudes toward wild birds, private individuals
formed several protective organizations, including the Selborne Society
and the Society for the Protection of Birds. Of the practice of mounting
birds and putting them in glass cases to ornament English parlors, Hudson once wrote: "It outrages my sense of fitness, and is as detestable as
stuffed birds and wings, tails and head, and beaks of murdered and mu-
tilated birds on women's headgear."

The barrage leveled at them by Grinnell, Whittier, Hudson and
other outraged males slowly began to take effect on some women of
fashion. One of the most conscience-stricken was Mrs. Augustus Hemenway, a prominent Boston matron who had been reading in the press
certain accounts of the plume hunters' depredations. Inviting several
friends to her Clarendon Street home one wintry afternoon in 1896, she
talked over the matter with them, and they decided to take some action
of their own. Mrs. Hemenway opened her copy of the *Boston Blue Book,*
and a woman who was present that day recalled many years later: "We
marked the names of the ladies of fashion who would be
likely to wear aigrettes on their hats or in their hair. We then sent out
circulars asking the women to join a society for the protection of
birds . . . Some women joined, and some who preferred to wear the
feathers would not join."

Mrs. Hemenway called the first meeting of the Massachusetts Audubon Society at her home on February 10, 1896. In attendance were not only the city's conscionable society women but also a group of men who were interested in both ornithology and the field sports. (Most ornithologists of the time used the gun expertly and often to enlarge their scientific collections.) No little old ladies in tennis shoes were observed on the premises.

This group, which is truly the ancestor of all of today's Audubon societies, states its purpose in the bylaws: "To discourage the buying and wearing, for ornamental purposes, of the feathers of any wild birds except ducks and gamebirds, and to otherwise further the protection of native birds."

Several months later the qualifying phrase, "except ducks and gamebirds," was stricken from the bylaws. The members elected as their first president William Brewster, curator of the Museum of Comparative Zoology at Harvard and one of the AOU's founders. Among its vice-presidents the society numbered Charles Francis Adams, Sarah Orne Jewett and Mrs. Louis Agassiz. By the end of its first year it had 1,284 members, 358 of whom were schoolchildren.

The idea caught on almost immediately. The Pennsylvania Audubon Society was founded later in the same year. In 1897, Audubon societies sprang up in New York, New Hampshire, Illinois, Maine, Wisconsin, New Jersey, Rhode Island, Connecticut and the District of Columbia. Frank M. Chapman traveled to Washington to deliver the local society's first public lecture, speaking on the theme "Woman As a Bird Enemy." The Pennsylvania Audubon Society published a popular circular called *Woman's Heartlessness* which had been written by the poet Celia Laighton Thaxter shortly before her death in 1894. The circular recounted her argument with a typical cultivated but heartless woman who insisted on wearing plumes. "It was merely a waste of breath," the poet concluded, "and she went her way, a charnel house of beaks and claws and bones and feathers and glass eyes upon her fatuous head."

But Massachusetts remained the spearhead of the early movement.

Certainly a vital reason for its early success was the work carried on by one of its members, George H. Mackay, an expert on gulls and terns and also a member of the AOU. For some years, Mackay had taken it upon himself to protect the nesting colonies of Laughing Gulls and various terns on islands off the Massachusetts coast, especially on Muskeget and Penikese. Armed with copies of a statute passed by the Massachusetts legislature in 1886, which called for a fine of ten dollars to be levied against persons who killed gulls and terns or took their eggs (the law was almost never enforced before the end of the century except by Mackay), he did his best to keep the millinery gunners away. He even shot short-eared owls on Muskeget because they preyed on the sea birds. In 1899, with the number of birds increasing, he handed the islands over to the Audubon Society's protection, commenting that they were "in a most satisfactory condition."

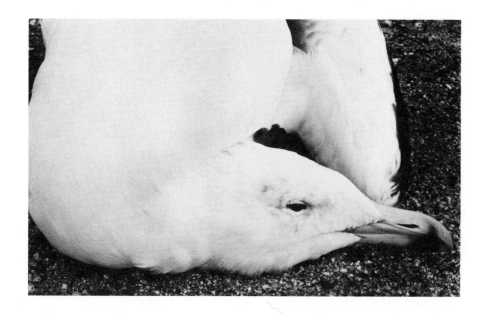

The remnant Herring Gull colonies in the United States lay off the Maine coast, remote and difficult to protect. Fortunately there was on the AOU's Bird Protection Committee a man with both the time and the will to work diligently on the gulls' behalf. William Dutcher, a native of New Jersey, had built a successful insurance business in New York. He was one of those inspired amateurs—well-read, genuinely interested in natural history—who fight the battles that the professionals in government are often unwilling or unable to undertake. He encouraged the founding of Audubon societies

8

all over the country (and later became the first president of the National Association of Audubon Societies). Even before that he had joined with other AOU members in framing a model law on which they hoped the various states would base their own bird-protective legislation, and which was perhaps the AOU's most lasting contribution to conservation.

There was bitter opposition to such laws against killing wild birds. Some of it came from within the AOU itself; several prominent members thought that the bill would restrict scientific collectors ("I don't protect birds," one defiant ornithologist insisted, "I kill them"). Protests came from taxidermists and zoölogists. To sweep around the flanks of potential opposition to the bill from the owners of hotels, restaurants and cold storages, the AOU omitted game birds—waterfowl, shore birds, grouse, pheasants, quail, turkeys, rails and coots—from its protective shield. But the most effective opposition came from the milliners. When a bill was introduced in Congress in 1898 to prohibit the importation of millinery plumes, as well as the sale or shipment of them within the United States, the *Millinery Trade Review* called on dealers to crush "his most iniquitous and childish measure."

Dutcher knew that ultimately only strong legislation would save the many species of birds being killed for their plumage. Early in 1900 the lobbying he and his colleagues had done bore fruit in Washington. Congress passed the Lacey Act, which gave bird protection an enormous lift on the national level. Sponsored by Representative John F. Lacey of Iowa, the law prohibited interstate traffic in birds killed in violation of state laws.

What still remained to be taken care of was the crude patchwork of generally inadequate state laws. Probably the most damaging loophole was in New York, the center of the millinery industry. Although many birds were protected by New York state law, gulls and terns were classed among "web-footed wildfowl," and thus remained fair game. And Maine, the only state in which Herring Gulls then nested, had no law protecting them. The Lacey Act was, in these cases, almost useless.

Dutcher decided, as a stopgap measure, to try to cut off the supply of gulls' plumage at its source—by protecting the gulls on their nesting islands. Early in 1900 he arranged for wardens to patrol islands in those states which had already passed protective laws. Until gulls were protected in Maine at the end of that year, he persuaded the owners to prohibit trespassing. Working from his office in New York, with the limited funds available to him, he faced an unenviable task, but he was indefatigable. He wrote to ornithologists in Maine asking them to locate the gulls' important breeding sites. On the theory that the best wardens would be local men who knew the area, had the respect of their neighbors and were on the breeding grounds a good deal of the time, he corresponded with lighthouse keepers and sometimes with the owners of the islands. He had No TRESPASSING posters printed, asking that the birds on the posted islands be allowed to nest undisturbed, and shipped them to various lightkeepers on the Maine coast.

Dutcher's correspondence became voluminous. Leafing through his letters today, one gets an idea of the frustrations he must have faced in carrying out such a venture without the help of telephones, automobiles, motor launches and aircraft. An inquiry to the ornithologist Manley Hardy about colonies of gulls and terns near lighthouses brought the following reply in March 1900:

> I know of no colony near any lighthouse. There used to be a large colony on Matinicus [Rock] not far from Rockland. The keeper of the light, a Mr. Grant, did all in his power to protect them but men would come and lay in boats and put out wounded gulls for decoys and shoot the most of them in spite of all he could do.

Dutcher wrote to William Grant and got his promise to try to protect the birds that summer. He signed a contract with George E. Cushman of Cape Elizabeth, agreeing to pay him thirty dollars to protect the birds on Bluff and Stratton Islands. Turning to gull colonies farther east, he wrote to Captain William C. Gott of Milbridge, the keeper of the Pond Island light: "If you will agree to care for these birds and protect them, and keep people from taking their eggs or shooting the birds until the first of October, I will pay you on receipt of your report on that date the sum of twenty-five dollars ($25.00)." Dutcher paid a total of five hundred dollars, raised through the various bird-protection societies, to the wardens on the Maine coast that summer.

After the middle of May he received a letter from William F. Stanley, the lightkeeper on Great Duck Island off Mount Desert:

> *We have two thousand gulls mated and building nests. On the 16th inst. two canoes with Indians landed here. My man went to their camp with one of your posters and read it to them. When the poster was read the Indians laughed at him and talked to him badly. They all had guns and said they had come to the island to kill gulls and get what eggs they can.*
>
> *I went to them on the 17th inst. and tried to explain to them they would not listen to me and we have had some words. I told them I would dog their tracks. While I was over there I see another canoe with three Indians in it landing here. They are bound to get the gulls by gun torch or snare. A boy is now letting me [know?] that the Indians are firing guns. But their work is in the night. I cannot learn their names. If I had a Kodak I could get their faces or catch them in the act. But I had rather shoot* them. *Posters don't count.*

Dutcher sent off telegrams to the owners of the island asking permission for a lawyer representing the AOU in Maine to enforce no-trespassing statutes and stop the Indians' depredations: . . . I WILL PAY YOU FIFTY DOLLARS TO PREVENT THEM FROM DOING SO THIS BREEDING SEASON. ACTION MUST BE TAKEN AT ONCE. ANSWER AT MY EXPENSE. Ap-

Gulls at the Boston fish pier

parently a number of gulls were killed before the Indians could be induced to leave the island.

Dutcher paid a visit to the bird islands off the Maine coast that summer. He traveled part of the way on one of the big steamers that once plied the coast, walking the promenade deck and catching glimpses of passing gulls and terns. On the boat he struck up an acquaintance with an Indian who worked for most of the year as a mason around Bar Harbor but who took time off occasionally to shoot gulls when the milliners' prices were high. He was able to earn more money shooting gulls, he told Dutcher, than he could as a mason. At least ten thousand large gulls had been killed during 1899 along the Maine coast and on nearby Canadian islands, the Indian said. Dutcher dutifully recorded the details of the conversation in his notebook:

> The price went from about $5 per dozen to $12. A dozen consists of two wings and 3 pieces, two of the breast and one back. It takes about 4 gulls to make a dozen. The pieces are stripped from the dead bird and are then washed and cured. Some of the birds are shot, some are snared on or about the nests, and some are caught on trawl lines that are baited. This season the demand is not so great, and the price has gone down to $3.00 per dozen.
>
> The Indian also told me that a great many small gulls were shot, some of which were terns and some that come late in the fall, which must have been Kittiwakes and Bonaparte's and Ringbills. He said that a law had been passed which prevented the birds being shot in Maine during the breeding season. [There was a law in Maine at the time which protected terns, but not gulls.] He and his crew had shot about 600 birds this year. A great many birds were secured by having a live gull tied in the top of a small pine tree in the woods on an island. The Indians would hide underneath the tree and when the other gulls came about they were shot.

The island in which Dutcher was most interested was No Man's Land, the site of the largest Herring Gull colony in the United States. He left the steamer at Rockland and went by tug to Matinicus Island, a trip of about eighteen miles. There he was introduced to "Uncle Mark" Young, the owner of No Man's Land and an elderly bachelor whom Dutcher considered eccentric but extremely entertaining. Young had given up fishing and now ran a general store on Matinicus, opening it at four o'clock every afternoon "to do a little trading with the people." Dutcher agreed to pay him fifty dollars to watch the birds that summer.

Early on the morning after his arrival, Dutcher arranged for Young to take him to the island. The old man met him at the wharf with a large dory, and the two of them took turns rowing the mile or more through a rough sea to the gull colony. At their approach the gulls rose from the island's rocks and spruces, circling and screaming overhead. Dutcher, on his first visit to a large gull colony, was greatly moved. He estimated the birds' numbers at nearly four thousand. Uncle Mark, guiding his dory over the moving, toppling crests of surf and avoiding the outpost rocks, landed Dutcher among the boulders on No Man's Land's shore. They walked past Young's grazing sheep to the higher part of the twelve-acre island.

> I commenced to see the young gulls [Dutcher wrote afterward in his notebook]. Some were as big as hens and from that down to little ones just out of the shell. It was a novel experience for me to see these young birds. The very small ones would try to hide as soon as I came near them. If they hid their head in the grass or under a stump they thought that the whole body was hidden. The larger ones would run just as soon as I came near them so it was almost impossible to photograph them . . . It required a great deal of care where to step so as not to step on young birds that were trying to hide in the grass.

Young told Dutcher that he had kept gunners from shooting the birds with the aid of the No Trespassing posters. The only trouble-makers, he reported, were "fishermen who do not live on Matinicus." The colony, Dutcher concluded, was in excellent condition and his experience there strengthened his belief in the value of a warden system.

Dutcher, whose skill at prying the facts from rascals
seems more appropriate for a district attorney than an insurance salesman, tried his hand again later in 1900. He had been
informed by a woman in Southwest Harbor, Maine, that a
man named Al Williams, who represented millinery firms in
Boston and New York, had set up shop near her home. She
told Dutcher of seeing the bodies and skins of many gulls
which hung on his piazza. Dutcher immediately shot off a
note to Williams reminding him that the Lacey Act, prohib-
iting the interstate traffic in wild birds, had recently been

9

passed by Congress. "The Society which I represent," Dutcher told him, speaking of the AOU, "will have a detective employed who will notify us when you ship your skins and where, and as soon as they leave the State of Maine they will be seized under the new law."

Williams wrote back, contending that Dutcher had been misinformed and that in any case he must have confused him with some marauding Indians. He assured Dutcher that he had reported those Indians to the warden at Great Duck Island. The only plumage he bought was from fishermen, who killed the birds "60 to two hundred miles off shore." Finally, he reminded Dutcher that there was no law against killing gulls in Maine, and he said he would be grateful if he sent him a copy of the Lacey Act, "as your notice is the first I have received and I don't wish to disobey the law."

Dutcher had reason to believe Williams would continue unrepentant. So he wrote to him again, this time pretending to be a milliner just starting out and asking Williams to send him some samples of his large gulls and Kittiwakes, and to please include the names of other milliners to whom he shipped skins so that he would be able to verify the quality of his work. Williams' reply gives us a glimpse into the millinery trade as it existed in those days:

> According to your order I ship this day one box of skins and wings for which I received your money order for five dollars.
>
> They are not the best, neither are they the poorest. The white gull is not a fine specimen, he is not fully turned yet but they go for white as soon as there tail wings and breast turns. I had some white gulls on hand that I shipped the day I received your letter, we get the whitest gulls in February and March their neck is the last part that turns.
>
> You understand that my skins are what is called in the rough, they are not feather dressed; my time is mostly on the inside of the skin after cleaning off blood and sewing up shot holes.
>
> I refer you to C. W. Hammond, Boston fancy feather co. 76 Sum-

mer st, Boston. I worked for him a year buying bird skins, all along the coast from Boston to St. Andrew. I don't feel at liberty to give the name of the parties I ship to without consulting them on account of that Fake society formed by the feather dealers in New York, there is not one of them but would buy a thousand gull skins at once if they could get them . . .

I send one kittiwake mounted for the hat. I send the big gulls whole as I didn't know how you wanted them; all I ship I cut in three pieces, two breasts and back.

During the winter of 1900–1 the Maine Legislature passed the AOU's Model Law, which granted protection to gulls and most other wild birds. Since New York had also corrected deficiencies in its laws, Dutcher's hand was considerably strengthened and he was able to put to good use the information he had collected in the last year or two. He pressed federal authorities to crack down on milliners and their agents who were in violation of the Lacey Act. His most dramatic single stroke was sending the authorities to a Baltimore warehouse where twenty-six thousand gull skins were seized.

With the approach of the breeding season in 1901 Dutcher expanded his warden system in Maine and sent off aggressively worded posters to the lightkeepers, promising federal prosecution of those who killed or traded in protected species. He also sent scores of letters from New York, exhorting his wardens to vigilance and scolding those who let him down. One of the latter apparently was Captain George E. Pottle of Friendship, Maine, who had promised to keep an eye on the islands in Muscongus Bay. In July 1901 Dutcher sent him a letter that bristled with indignation:

A member of our society has just returned from a visit to the Eastern and Western Egg Rocks, and he writes me that the actual conditions there are deplorable. He states that the islands have been visited and from all the evidence he could obtain, have been systematically robbed. He also states that he found places where petrels have been dug out.

I would like to know what you have to say about the condition of these islands, and what you have done to protect them as you agreed. I cannot pay you for work that you do not do, nor do I care to pay if the birds are not protected. I expected that you would keep people from taking eggs, which is contrary to law, just as much as I expected you to prevent people from shooting the birds.

If you were aware that people were disturbing the birds breeding there, it was your duty to inform me so that I could take steps to have them prosecuted under law.

But on the whole, Dutcher's experience with his Maine wardens was gratifying. They had substantially advanced the birds' welfare. In a letter to Mrs. William F. Stanley, a warden–lightkeeper's wife whom he had met on his trip to Maine the year before and who had taken a keen interest in the protection of sea birds, Dutcher described the Herring Gull colonies along the coast in the summer of 1901:

The most westward one is on No-Man's Land about a mile N.E. from Matinicus Island; this colony is from 3,000 to 3,500 birds; is thoroughly protected and is increasing rapidly and the birds are remarkably tame.

There are two small colonies in Penobscot Bay; one on Little Spoon island and the other on Heron island. These birds receive no protection further than the placing of our warning notices on the islands. On both of these islands the old birds are not killed but the eggs are still taken to some extent, consequently the birds are wild.

The next colony is the Duck Island which you know all about. [The island's lightkeeper and warden was Mrs. Stanley's husband.] To the eastward there are a number of small colonies numbering anywhere from 100 to 500 birds. I found on my visit that the eggs are still taken

Gulls going after fish trapped in a weir

and it seems impossible to prevent it. The birds, however, are not molested.

The colonies are located on Nash's island, on Pulpit Rock on the Brothers island, the Double Headed Shot islands and Old Man's island. I think all of these small colonies are greatly increased although I found evidences of egg robbing on all of them, i.e. many broken up nests, especially on Nash's island where the owners, three women, are very much opposed to having the birds on the island as they said they hurt the sheep pasturing.

I did not visit, but I understand there is quite a large colony of birds upon Machias Seal island [where there was, and still is, a Canadian lighthouse] and that they are thoroughly cared for by the keeper of the light at that station. They are quite a distance off shore and consequently it is very easy to care for them.

On the whole I am very much pleased with the condition of affairs as I found them in Maine and I think that in a few years we will have a large number of birds again and that the sentiment among the fishermen will greatly incline toward the protection of birds.

I think it would be an excellent idea for us to get some real good evidence against one of the eggers and make an example of him.

The gulls of the northeast Atlantic coast were about to enter upon a new relationship with man.

On a summer morning several years ago a station wagon bulging with camping and scientific gear appeared in the driveway of our home in Maine, and a blond young British ornithologist named Jeremy Hatch introduced himself. He had heard in town that my wife and I might be sympathetic to a study of terns he was about to begin on Petit Manan Island. Did we have a boat he could use? We did, and we located an outboard motor to push it along. During that summer and succeeding ones we kept ourselves acquainted with Jeremy Hatch's investigations on the island and learned certain facts that we came to feel transcended a study of birds apparently remote from human concerns.

10

Petit Manan rises two and a half miles off the coast of eastern Maine, a lump of rock and turf about three hundred and thirty yards long that early French explorers named and local people have referred to almost ever since as 'Tit Manan. One of the tallest lighthouses on the Atlantic coast stands on the island. Since the light was automated at the end of 1972 and the crew of three coastguardsmen removed, its only inhabitants are the colonies of nesting sea birds, principally three species of terns—Arctic, roseate and common—perhaps three thousand in all. Terns, with their long, slender wings and forked tails, are among the most graceful of all fliers; they are sometimes called "sea swallows." The Arctic terns have one of the longest migration routes in the world, some of them flying nearly from one polar region to the other and back again during the year, a total distance of more than twenty thousand miles. All in all, they are among the coast's most splendid adornments. In the taller vegetation at the center of the island nest a few pairs of Laughing Gulls, their most northerly outpost along the Atlantic coast.

From afar, Petit Manan seems to exist in lonely grandeur, undulating on the swell if the haze creates an optical illusion, a misty apparition untouched by man's dinginess. But no lives remain isolated from human impact today. The succession of ironic circumstances that finally affects this island's birds illustrates in miniature the results of man's heedlessness along all the world's coastlines.

At low tide Petit Manan is connected by a gravelly bar to its smaller neighbor, Green Island, which is inhabited by nesting colonies of eider ducks, Herring Gulls and Great Black-backed Gulls. Camping on Petit Manan, watching the gulls from a distance through his binoculars, Hatch was able to confirm the fears that other ornithologists have expressed recently for the future of Maine's tern colonies.

The incessant raids by the larger gulls on the terns' nests (simply bits of grass, twigs and shells scraped together on the ground) were devastating. As Hatch watched, a large gull swept in low across the water from Green Island. Terns and Laughing Gulls rose from the Petit

The nest of the Arctic tern

Manan colony, mobbing the intruder, diving and screaming. Ignoring the defenders, the large gull made a pass at an undefended terns' nest and seized a downy chick. Still mobbed by the terns, it got back into the air, its feathers flying as terns pecked impotently at its back, and gulped down the struggling chick in midflight.

Curiously, the gulls did not molest the terns' unhatched eggs. On other islands, gulls have been seen smashing and eating terns' eggs, and Hatch suspected the same thing might have occurred on Petit Manan before he arrived.

"Perhaps late in the season," he wrote afterward, "the probability of striking a watery rotten egg is so great they prefer the more certain rewards of live chicks or fresh fish, although it is not known even if gulls prefer fresh eggs to rotten ones."

Hatch's meticulous observations confirmed the enormous toll. By clocking the number of successful raids each hour, he estimated that gulls devoured between seven hundred and fifteen hundred tern chicks on the island during the summer. Because under ordinary conditions the majority of chicks die of cold, wet or starvation during the first few days of their lives, the predation snuffed out the lives of a large proportion of the older chicks which might otherwise have survived at least to the fledging stage. The terns of Petit Manan, in fact, might not be producing enough young to sustain the colony.

The small Laughing Gull colony in the terns' midst proved to be something of a Trojan Horse. Although Hatch never noticed these smaller gulls taking terns' eggs or chicks, he often saw examples of cleptoparasitism (a word he defined as "seizing food gathered by another, which can be considered a special form of food competition"). As a tern flew in from the sea, carrying in its bill one of the small herring or other fish on which it feeds its young, it would be attacked by one of the Laughing Gulls, or perhaps by several of them. The gulls chased the tern, forcing it to drop the fish or sometimes even tearing the fish from the tern's bill. Because these attacks did not begin until the end of June,

Arctic Tern

Hatch speculated that the Laughing Gulls pirated fish as an easy way to feed their own chicks, which were only a few days old.

What especially interested Hatch in these gang attacks was that they did not lead to "instant gratification" for most of the attackers. The small fish was invariably eaten by only one of the Laughing Gulls, not shared like the large prey chased down by pack-hunting mammals such as wild dogs. The gratification for the majority of gulls must have come from the shorter time required by a group chase, which produced much more certain results than one undertaken alone; an individual Laughing Gull was likely to commandeer the prize only if the chases took place often enough. Hatch also noted that although he himself never saw any of the Laughing Gulls rob terns of their eggs, such thievery was reported at other tern colonies. He concluded that egg robbing by Laughing Gulls "varies from colony to colony, and possibly from year to year."

Hatch's observations raised some disquieting possibilities. Although the small number of Laughing Gulls nesting on Petit Manan seemed to pose no immediate threat to the terns, what would be their effect during those breeding seasons when there was a shortage of food? Many more young terns might not survive.

The other question had a more direct bearing on the situation at Petit Manan and several other tern colonies along the coast. Apparently the only factor that prevented the larger gulls from spreading their nesting grounds from Green Island to Petit Manan was the presence of the coastguardsmen. One or two Herring Gulls had already been seen building a nest there. When the coastguardsmen were removed, would the large gulls, which arrive earlier in the spring, take over the best nesting sites on *both* islands, and thus eventually dislodge the terns entirely? There were good reasons for believing that this might be the case.

The growth or decline of an animal's numbers, or the expansion or contraction of its range, is of great interest to anyone concerned about the natural world. Why do these changes occur? Decline, with perhaps extinction waiting not far down the road, holds a certain morbid fascination for all of us, and in the past this phenomenon has been reasonably well documented. It is easy to see why the great auk became extinct. Someone has said that a bird has not needed to "develop" intelligence because it can solve all of its problems simply by flying away from them. But the flightless great auk

11

had lost even that ability, so it was not able to deal with the frightening new predator—man—who invaded its nesting islands and methodically bludgeoned it out of existence.

The case of the passenger pigeon was a little more complex. Man again was the villain, but this time he combined with his relentless assault the destruction of the extensive forests on which the pigeons depended for beechnuts and acorns. ("When the pigeoners subtracted from his numbers, and the pioneers chopped gaps in the continuity of his fuel," Aldo Leopold has written, "his flame guttered out with hardly a sputter or even a wisp of smoke.")

Whales, wolves, orang-utans and tigers fight for existence in a world where man has indiscriminately slaughtered them for food or fun, or destroyed the wilderness which the animals need to nourish and reproduce themselves. Less obvious but still well documented are climatic changes (the advance or retreat of an Ice Age, for example) that may contribute to a species' decline.

Until quite recently, the reasons for a species' growth and expansion were not so well understood. Easiest to explain were the remarkable successes of "introduced" species—like the house sparrow (formerly called the English sparrow) and the starling, which were intentionally introduced to the United States from Europe in the nineteenth century, and being extremely adaptable, flourished and spread at the expense of native birds. The red-whiskered bulbul, an exotic bird which escaped from pet dealers near Miami, Florida, in 1960, has established a thriving colony there because suburbanites plant a variety of the tropical shrubs and plants that form an important part of its natural habitat in India. Some native birds, too, have profited from man's alteration of the landscape. The chestnut-sided warbler, comparatively rare in the early nineteenth century, has become a common bird because it prefers to live not in the deep forest, but at its edges. The American robin rapidly took to the broad, wormy lawns of urban and suburban North America.

Birds sometimes respond dramatically to man's works. Cardinals and other "Southern" species recently expanded their ranges northward mainly because home bird feeders enable them to survive the long winters when they otherwise would not be able to find food. Chimney swifts and a variety of swallows (including the cliff swallows, which return every year to Capistrano) nest in and around the buildings erected by man. The brown-headed cowbird, which was originally the "buffalo bird," abandoned those vanishing mammals and began following livestock to feed on the insects stirred up by the moving herds; more recently they have joined common grackles in adjusting to another development of the beef industry—they flock in thousands to cattle feed lots where they devour (and often contaminate with their droppings) the loose grain. Although there is no hard evidence that the numbers of red-winged blackbirds increased markedly during the last hundred years, they are densely concentrated in Midwestern cornfields, especially in Ohio, where they threaten to ruin farmers who inadvertently planted their crops athwart the birds' age-old migration routes.

Decline or growth—their sources still concern us, and in several species of gulls, notably the Herring Gull, we find a beguiling mixture of both. Apparently this bird once lived in comparative equilibrium with its environment, but during the nineteenth century, man sent it spiraling into a nearly catastrophic population decline; then it rebounded, this time by man's grace, to unwieldy numbers in the present century. Today its success is matched by few other native American vertebrate animals.

The Herring Gull began its climb early in this century, just as the bird protection movement made solid gains. Most states passed some version of the Model Law. In 1918 the Migratory Bird Treaty with Canada was ratified by Congress, protecting most nongame species. The key to the success of those legislative gains, of course, was the warden system. Under William Dutcher's direction, the Audubon societies expanded the system, raising funds to pay for wardens to protect the important nesting colonies during the critical years. In 1904, contributions came from people in a number of states, with Massachusetts citizens providing the bulk of the funds—$2,027—while those in New York added $1,212. Maine contributed only $10, and nothing was heard from Florida. In both these cases, enlightened philanthropists lent a helping hand to their benighted fellows, for only $33.25 was spent in law-abiding Massachusetts, while $475.46 was needed to protect gull and tern colonies in Maine, and $670.36 to keep the plume hunters away from Florida's heronries. (It was while serving as an Audubon warden in Florida that Guy Bradley was murdered by a plume hunter near Cape Sable in 1905. Bradley, a resident of Flamingo at the edge of the Everglades, and a plume hunter himself as a boy, became dedicated to the birds' protection. Catching a hunter with dead herons in his possession in Florida Bay one day, Bradley attempted to arrest him. The hunter, a man named Smith, turned the gun on Bradley and shot him through the chest. Bradley's body drifted for a day in a small boat along the shore until local boys, made curious by circling vultures, alerted such authorities as there were in southern Florida during that lawless time. Although the Audubon societies tried to see that the case was prosecuted vigorously, Smith went free; however, his neighbors in Flamingo burned down his house. The societies raised money to buy a home in Key West for Bradley's widow and children.)

But the Herring Gull also profited from changing American life styles. Many Maine families, for instance, whose forebears had fled to the offshore islands two centuries earlier to escape the raids of the French and Indian Wars, began to find island life too restricting. They drifted back to the mainland, taking with them the cats, dogs, sheep and other mammals (including rats) with which nesting birds find it difficult to coexist. The islands were once more left to the birds. A little later the confining interiors of automobiles finally dampened for good the enthusiasm of even the most unregenerate fashion plates for long-plumed hats.

At the same time, man was beginning to saturate his surroundings

Gulls around a fish cannery

with waste. In his autobiography Arthur Rubinstein recalls the adverse impression made on him by the huge dumps that rose like great sores around the American cities he visited on his first recital tour here early in the century. To Americans who noticed the filth around harbors and beaches, the return of the Herring Gull in numbers was a welcome event.

At first the gulls seemed to be back in equilibrium with their environment. As both scavengers and raucous ornaments of the shore they were a part of our wild heritage, but their admirers did not reckon with the human talent for unconscious mischief. Dumps, fish wharves, canneries and pig farms increased, providing a cornucopia for the rising population of gulls. The great restricting factors on the numbers of any wild animals are food and suitable breeding places. Herring Gulls were now in possession of almost unlimited quantities of both. Accommodating themselves to the circumstances, they began to abandon the outer islands that had afforded them some measure of sanctuary and, under protection, took over islands closer to the mainland's bounty. They also began to inch their way southward along the coast. In the 1920s they nested in increasing numbers on such Massachusetts islands as Muskeget and even reached Orient Point on New York's Long Island. The gulls founding new colonies on islands to the south were, in most cases, young birds just coming of breeding age and unable to shoulder their way into established colonies.

The Herring Gull was not the only member of the great subfamily of gulls which was extending its range. In a fugal pattern, the Great Black-backed Gull was coming in just behind it, recapitulating its movement down the coast. In 1833 Audubon had traveled to Labrador and seen this largest of the gulls, which had been wiped out as a breeding bird in the United States.

> High in the thin keen air, far above the rugged crags of the deserted shores of Labrador [*Audubon wrote of what he must have thought of as almost an exotic bird*] *proudly sails the tyrant Gull, floating down*

Herring Gull pulling grass

on almost motionless wing, like an eagle in his calm and majestic flight . . . Harsh and loud are his cries, and with no pleasant feeling do they come on the winged multitudes below . . . Now onward he sweeps . . . the breeding birds prepare to defend their unfledged broods, or ensure their escape from the powerful beak of their remorseless spoiler. Even the shoals of finny tribes sink deeper into the waters as he approaches.

It may be a clue to Audubon's feelings about the "tyrant" Great Black-backed Gull that he painted the bird writhing on the ground, its left wing smashed and bloody (from his own shot?). Aside from this and one or two other paintings, such as that of a black snake attacking a brown thrasher and his prophetic rendering of a dead Eskimo curlew, he portrayed his birds alive and well in their natural surroundings.

A century later the Black-back spread down the Atlantic coast under protection, according to the best estimates first nesting in Maine in 1928, in Massachusetts in 1931 and in New York in 1942. Ornithologists suggest that the advance guard was probably stimulated to breed on strange ground by the sight of the ardently courting and posturing Herring Gulls. Although Black-backs ordinarily begin nesting earlier in the season than Herring Gulls do, in these cases they simply moved in beside the smaller gulls and established their own territories. Often nesting on the same islands as the Herring Gulls, they preyed on their chicks and thereby provided one of the few checks on the smaller gulls' population.

On the Pacific coast, where the human pressure on them had never been as great as it was on the Atlantic, gulls became more conspicuous as civilization offered them its largesse. A. C. Bent described Glaucous-winged Gulls in 1921:

They are abundant, in winter, in the harbors of nearly all the large cities on the Pacific coast as far south as southern California, where they

Gulls on polluted tidal flats

feed largely on refuse and seem to fill the place occupied by the herring gull on the Atlantic coast. They are particularly numerous about the garbage heaps which are dumped on the shore to be washed away by the advancing tides. In such places they appear to realize that they are protected and they are very tame. In their eagerness to secure the choice morsels of food they seem to forget all about the presence of human beings, even within a few feet . . . During the summer they frequent the vicinity of salmon canneries, where they gorge themselves on the refuse from the factories or fishing vessels. On the Pribilof Islands they regularly visit the killing grounds to feast on the entrails and other waste portions of the slaughtered seals . . . They become much excited and clamorous in their scramble for food, competing at close quarters with other species of gulls, with dogs, and with the lazy Indians.

The Western Gull, once primarily a predator on small fish such as herring, also took the easy road offered by civilization and, Bent noted, "has learned to frequent harbors and populated shores, where it can easily gorge itself on the garbage dumping grounds, pick up unsavory morsels at the outlets of sewers, and feed on whatever refuse it can find scattered along the beaches." David F. Costello has described gulls massed so tightly at dumps in Portland, Oregon, "that the garbage men amuse themselves by rushing into the mob and catching gulls that get tangled in the mighty confusion of beating wings."

In England, garbage dumps increasingly lured Black-headed Gulls inland; they became "commuters" in winter, flying to London to feed on garbage during the day and returning to the suburbs in the evening to lakes and reservoirs. In New Zealand, according to the ornithologist Oliver L. Austin, Jr., "the red-billed Silver Gull and the black-billed Buller's Gull inhabit the parks of the coastal cities like so many pigeons."

But under the new order not all sea birds, and not even all gulls, prospered. Man had to intervene in their lives once more.

Late in the 1930s the ornithologists E. H. Forbush and J. B. May, in their book *Natural History of the Birds of Eastern and Central North America*, described a remarkable island off the coast of Massachusetts:

> *South of the peninsula of Cape Cod lies a sandy island which is now the chief breeding place of the Laughing Gull in New England. The Indians named this islet Muskeget and it still bears the name. Lying on the boundary of Nantucket Sound and surrounded by treacherous shoals, it is one*

12

of the graveyards of the Atlantic and is avoided by mariners. Often its shores are strewn with the wreckage of lost ships. Strange sea-creatures frequent the deeps and shallows that surround the island. Small fish often abound in the adjacent waters and these are pursued by larger fish and sea-birds. Thousands of gulls and terns breed and rear their young upon the sands of the island. It is one of the largest bird nurseries on the New England coast. Muskeget Island consists mainly of sand built up by wave and wind and appears to be of comparatively recent origin. It is roughly crescent-shaped and is about one and one half miles long. Sandspits rising above the waters near its north-western face defend it against the sea and provide a harbor for small boats. Tides run fiercely over the shoals about it and in windy weather, particularly at low stages of the tide, foaming breakers roar for miles along the tiderips and break in fury on the shore. Treeless, Muskeget is a succession of low, rolling dunes and hollows or sandy levels covered more or less with beach-grass, poison ivy, beach-peas and other low-growing plants and with stunted bayberry and beach-plum bushes. Formerly its vegetation was very sparse; but this has increased in quantity and luxuriance, making conditions more favorable for the Laughing Gulls, which prefer to hide their nests, and less so for the Common Terns, which affect more open, sandy land.

Muskeget is one of the most thoroughly studied "bird islands" on the Atlantic coast. There are records of birds nesting there which go all the way back to the first third of the nineteenth century. At that time it harbored probably the largest tern colony on the coast. Laughing Gulls also nested there in large numbers, but they were virtually exterminated by 1875. Late in the century they reinvaded the island, establishing their nests in the taller grass close to the terns. The terns held their own for a while, but the Laughing Gulls increased enormously, in part because of the denser vegetation, which they favor for nesting sites. In the 1920s, perhaps twenty thousand pairs nested on Muskeget. But Herring Gulls, moving slowly southward from Maine, began nesting on

Laughing Gull

the island in 1910. As their numbers increased, those of the Laughing Gulls declined. Arriving earlier in the spring, the larger Herring Gulls were able to seize and defend the preferred nesting sites. Laughing Gulls, like the terns they had displaced, dwindled to insignificance. (It is interesting to note that in recent years Great Black-backed Gulls have arrived on Muskeget and made the island the site of their largest nesting colony in the United States; they may in turn drive the Herring Gulls from the island.)

What happened on Muskeget also happened on many of the bird islands along the coast. Twelve hundred terns nested on Large Weepecket Island off southern Massachusetts in 1938, and not a single Herring Gull. Two years later there were a thousand pairs of terns and four hundred of gulls. In 1942 the gulls had built up their numbers to a thousand pairs, while there were only ten pairs of terns. The next year the terns disappeared from the island.

Along the Maine coast, terns were being pushed off all but a few of the islands, while by World War II, Laughing Gulls no longer bred in the state. Other sea birds were under similar pressure from Herring Gulls. Predation seems to have been only part of the pressure. Perhaps more important was the Herring Gull's trait of beginning to establish territories on the nesting islands earlier in the spring than most other birds. Thus, when the other birds arrived, the gulls had already secured the suitable nesting sites.

Herring Gulls were disturbing not only their avian neighbors, they were riling some human beings too. Marsden Hartley, the landscape painter who was born in Lewiston, Maine, wrote a poem some years ago in which he spoke of the "change" that had taken place among gulls along the Androscoggin River; once they had eaten fish, now they had discovered the blueberry pastures, "looking for the blue beads with wafts of skybreath clinging to them," and thus the sea birds had become "vegetarians." In less poetic terms the owners of blueberry land in eastern Maine lodged complaints about these gulls with the federal govern-

Great Black-backed Gulls

ment. Along the coast it was (and still is in some places) the custom to put sheep to pasture on small islands during the spring and summer, since this obviates the need for fences, shepherds and most of the other traditional safeguards used by sheepmen. Many of these people objected to the presence of gulls on their islands. In this case, Herring Gulls probably suffered for the sins of the encroaching Black-back population.

"Those Black-backed Gulls are wicked," a down-easter said recently. "If a ewe drops two lambs, the Black-backs move right in, and they're sure to get one of 'em. They chew right in through the rear end and turn the little fellows inside out—they eat them right up to the knuckles."

As in most complaints by sheep raisers, the damage is overstated. In fact, a Maine ornithologist, Arthur H. Norton, writing in *Bird-Lore* (the predecessor of *Audubon*) in 1918, explained how the gulls probably benefited the sheep population as a whole:

> *It was found that much of the soil of these islands is very sterile, composed largely of decomposed wood, many of the deposits being over 2½ feet deep, entirely destitute of mineral soil. By visiting several different islands where the gulls were abundant, and others where none or very few were nesting, it was possible to make a comparison of the conditions prevailing at the two different locations. On the islands where there were few Gulls, the vegetation was poor, closely grazed, and struggling hard for existence; moreover, the sheep there were eating the coarser forms of vegetation, left untouched on the islands where the Gulls were numerous. On those islands where the Gulls were numerous, the vegetation was invariably luxuriant. On each of the latter were areas nearly free from Gulls, yet the sheep showed no preference for those locations, but were found to feed in the midst of the colonies as much, or even more, than in the parts where the Gulls were nearly absent. On these islands, the coarse flags, sedges, rushes, and grasses were not touched by the sheep.*

Farther south, Forbush and May wrote, the gulls' role as scavengers was not always appreciated:

> Sometimes the zeal of the gulls in disposing of such noisome things brings them into disfavor with the farmers who, having hauled loads of dead fish to their fields for fertilizer, fail to plow them under, and soon find that they have vanished, the gulls having flown away with them. Not long ago a farmer in Rhode Island bought for fertilizer some tons of starfish that had been dredged up by the oystermen; but he let them lie too long and when he got ready to haul them, they had disappeared. The gulls knew where they went.

As early as 1934, the U.S. Biological Survey (the predecessor of the U.S. Fish and Wildlife Service) started a program to control the Herring Gull along the Atlantic coast. Workers landed on the nesting islands and "needled" the eggs. This operation was not as scientific as it sounds; it simply means that the workers were equipped with sharp sticks, or sticks with a nail pounded into their tips, and they walked across an island puncturing all the eggs they could find. The object of needling was to leave the eggs relatively intact so that the gulls would go on brooding and not lay another clutch. The gulls were not fooled for long, however, because the eggs soon rotted and burst.

In any case, the program was carried out rather randomly. In 1940, gull control took a great step forward. Under the direction of Alfred O. Gross, a distinguished ornithologist at Bowdoin College, the government program became highly sophisticated. Gross and his students systematically visited the islands along the Maine coast, searching out nests and spraying the eggs with a mixture of high-grade carrier oil and ten percent formaldehyde in water—the oil to suffocate the embryo, and the formaldehyde to prevent the eggs from rotting and bursting and thus alerting the incubating adults to the fact that all was not well.

For twelve years Gross carried on the program with money provided by the federal government. It was amazingly successful in view of the wide area over which it was carried out (nine hundred thousand eggs on scores of islands were sprayed) and man's remorseless dumping of garbage and fish offal. The gull population in Maine, which had been doubling every twelve to fifteen years, leveled off and perhaps even declined between 1944 and 1951.

Other factors may have been at work too, especially during World War II when Americans were not as profligate with their wastes as usual and did not provide gulls with all of the food they needed during the nesting season. (There was a similar decline in the gull population in northern Europe during the war.) But there is no doubt that the spray program was producing the effect Gross was after. In 1944 he marked two plots on the Heron Islands, spraying the eggs on one plot and leaving them unsprayed on the other. The results showed that the spray made a tremendous difference; the production of chicks on the first plot was substantially below that on the second. To Gross's horror, he got further confirmation elsewhere. An inexperienced gull controller mistook terns' eggs for those of gulls, wiping out the only tern colony in Muscongus Bay.

Gross went by boat with his students through the islands late every spring, searching for any indication of nesting Herring Gulls. They investigated the low heaps of rock and turf as well as the higher islands where the cliff façades were not sheer but pocked like sponges, each niche supporting an almost tropical fountain of ferns and weeds and sometimes the nest of a black guillemot. In heavy surf it was difficult to land on many of the islands, and once ashore, the control crews faced other hazards—from diving, defecating birds and from the terrain. In his unpublished autobiography Gross describes a visit to the Brothers Island, southeast of Jonesport, in 1945. Chasing a chick across a grassy plateau (he does not say whether he intended to band it or throttle it), his foot caught in a cleft rock. He heard his leg "pop" as he went down, the rock holding him like a vise. Gross's assistants pried him free and carried him, his broken leg painful and swelling, down the side of a cliff and into the crashing surf. When the boat reached Jonesport the men found that the tide was out, and they had to wait offshore until ten o'clock that night before they could land. A doctor met them at the wharf and gave Gross a painkilling injection before fitting a temporary cast on his leg.

Despite what we now know was the program's success, there were puzzling sides to it at the time. Gross, taking into account the four or five years a Herring Gull needs to reach breeding age, calculated that the population would begin to show a pronounced decline after five or six years.

"Hence the egg counts of 1944 would be expected to be less than the counts of the same islands in 1940," Gross wrote near the end of World War II. "However, this is not the case, for there is an increase from 50,446 in 1940 to 57,937 eggs, or more than 12 per cent in 1944. This unexpected result raises the question as to the effectiveness of the technique of spraying as now employed."

The U.S. Fish and Wildlife Service began to believe that the program was a waste of time, its results not spectacular enough to justify the cost. The trouble was not with the program, however, but with the biologists' limited knowledge. They had anticipated a sharp and immediate decline in the gulls' numbers because they had underestimated their longevity. Adult gulls have no endemic diseases and few predators. It has since been determined, by the study of banding records as well as by computations of the ratio between juveniles and adults in the population, that the average life span of a Herring Gull which reaches maturity is about fifteen years. The older gulls were hanging on, so the population was not yet declining. Given several more years and a wider application of his principles in Massachusetts and Canada, Gross might have been able to bring about a stabilization of the East Coast gull population as the older ones died off without being replaced. But while he had halted the increase in Maine, the birds were extending their breeding colonies rapidly southward into southern New England, a development that may be attributed in part to Gross's disturbance of their original nesting islands. The spraying program was abandoned in 1952, and the Herring Gull immediately renewed its explosive increase all along the northeastern coast.

In his *Memories,* Sir Julian Huxley speaks of the unexpected ways in which wild things adjust themselves to altered
conditions, even to human disasters. In the bombed-out sec-
tions of London during World War II, country flowers and
trees suddenly took root in such profusion that Huxley was
reminded of "the jungle at Angkor," while the black redstart,
which nests in walls and empty houses and which "had been
a rare straggler in Britain before 1939, suddenly was able to
find so many nesting sites that it became quite common in
central London!" Several wars later and a continent away,

13

great flocks of flamingos established nesting grounds in the marshes of the Sinai Peninsula. Before 1967, Arab fishermen had consistently visited the marshes to rob the flamingos' nests of eggs and young. But when the Israelis seized the Sinai during the Six-Day War, the Arabs were excluded from the marshes and the flamingos flourished.

A similar capacity to adapt and endure has helped gulls to increase their populations and ranges even in recent years. Gulls seem to be not very susceptible to the epidemics that decimate populations of other birds such as ducks, though like all mortals, of course, they are subject to disease; botulism and aspergillosis, or "fungus disease," are among the most important. Both Herring Gulls in Boston Harbor and Glaucous-winged Gulls in San Francisco have been observed dying of the latter disease, which reduces the lungs to a mass of paper-thin tissue and a "greenish, powdery fungus." (The ties that bind birds to the great crocodilians may be further reinforced by the discovery that aspergillosis has also been found in the American alligator.) Moreover, gulls have so far largely escaped the ravages spread among many species of birds, including the bald eagle, the peregrine falcon, the brown pelican and the osprey, by modern chemical pesticides. The analysis of some birds' eggs has shown a dramatic thinning of the shells when they are contaminated by DDT's by-products (DDE). But gulls apparently have a higher threshold than many other bird species. A study of brown pelicans' eggs disclosed that DDT's by-products, in quantities as small as four or five parts per million, reduced the shells' thickness by fifteen percent, while gulls' eggs containing as high as eighty parts per million had their shells thinned by only eleven percent. However, Glaucous Gulls feeding on the eggs of other birds in the North Atlantic have been found dying of tremors, with high levels of DDT in their livers.

The jury is still out on DDT's effects on gulls over a long period of time; while the evidence is not conclusive, it is possible that DDT has helped to retard the earlier runaway growth of the Herring Gull population in the Northeast. For the time being, however, the leveling off of

The Herring Gull in the effluent society

the Herring Gull can be traced more surely to the present limits on its available food and breeding islands. The Northeast, in effect, has reached the saturation point in Herring Gulls.

In a recent study of the Ring-billed Gull in the Great Lakes, James P. Ludwig, a consulting ecologist, has suggested the ways in which gulls may be able to take advantage of man-made changes in the world around them. The Great Lakes, as everyone knows, are badly polluted by a number of domestic, industrial and agricultural sources, yet Ring-billed Gulls there enjoyed an astonishing increase in population beginning about 1960. At that time there were believed to be twenty-seven thousand nesting pairs of Ring-bills around Lakes Huron and Michigan. Seven years later their numbers had leaped to one hundred and forty-one thousand pairs. Ludwig traced this surge to two sources, one of them natural, the other human.

The Great Lakes experience a regular fluctuation in their water levels, rising and falling in cycles that take anywhere from five to eleven years to complete. In 1960 the water level of the lakes was very high. The following year the water began to drop, reaching the lowest level on record during the years 1964–65. Many small islands that had been submerged during periods of high water suddenly reappeared, providing the gulls with ample nesting space.

Typical of these sometime islands is the Charity Islands Reef, which emerged in 1961. While underwater, it had been scoured of its vegetation by waves and ice, leaving it conveniently free of the woody plants with which gulls must compete when staking out their nesting sites. Soon the gulls occupied the island at a density of forty-seven hundred nests an acre. Then, heavily fertilized by the Ring-bills' droppings, the island began to sprout a luxuriant growth, first of low grasses and herbage, later of woody plants such as willows. It became a race to see which rising natural force, water or vegetation, would eventually drive out the gulls.

The Ring-bills of the Great Lakes are of necessity a footloose pop-

Gulls at sewer pipe

ulation, ready to move at a moment's notice to dryer or less-green quarters. They must even keep a wary eye on man. Expo '67, the world's fair at Montreal, was built on an island that these gulls had used for nesting in the early 1960s, and they were forced out. At Toronto, on the other hand, they took over islands created by dredging operations.

Meanwhile, man's insensitive hand had altered the Great Lakes in such a way that they had become ripe for supporting the Ring-bills' soaring population. The Welland Canal permitted sea lampreys to enter the lakes. These voracious, eel-like creatures decimated the large predatory fish on which the Great Lakes' commercial fishery was based. With their normal predators destroyed, the smaller anadromous alewives invaded the lakes in large numbers, and it is on those fish that the nesting colonies of Ring-billed Gulls customarily feed. Nature provided the space, man the food, and the gulls flourished.

That the birds' population would increase under such munificence is not surprising, but a question remained: How are Ring-billed Gulls fitted by nature to expand so dramatically in such a short time if given an opportunity? Ludwig speculates that Ring-bills, like Herring, Great Black-backs and other large gulls, have been selected through evolution to adjust to unstable or "catastrophic" conditions. Some of these species evolved in the Arctic, where glaciation "alternately destroyed and remade gull habitat." Others, such as the Ring-bills, often nest in prairie potholes, which alternately fill and dry up. The several species, then, may have adjusted to boom-and-bust periods, normally producing more young than they need to maintain their species numbers, so that under favorable conditions they are able to make up for past catastrophic breeding seasons.

Like many other members of the subfamily of gulls, Ring-bills are fitted by nature for occasional spectacular "irruptions" when all of the conditions are right.

The success of any opportunistic species is often made at the expense of another species that is not so quick to adapt to the new pressures suddenly thrust upon it. The starling, for instance, has been implicated in the decline of the Eastern bluebird in many areas because it is usually on the scene before the attractive little thrush arrives from the South and thus seizes the tree cavities and nesting boxes in which the bluebird used to breed. Another alien, the house sparrow, often appropriates the nesting boxes that homeowners erect for the use of the tree swallow. Gulls, too, flourish at the ex-

14

pense of other birds, though the relationships are sometimes more complex than biologists at first believed.

The complexity of "gull predation" is illustrated in Great Britain, where Herring Gulls sometimes take the eggs of gannets. The predation is really triggered by human beings who, in entering the colony, frighten the gannets away from their nests. The gulls, which ordinarily would not be able to invade a colony of the larger birds with much success, simply follow the humans around and rifle the abandoned nests.

At the Deer Flat Refuge in southwestern Idaho, California Gulls raid the nests of a variety of other birds, including ring-necked pheasants, American coots, eared grebes, black-necked stilts and cinnamon

Eider ducks, a mature male in the background

teals. Sometimes a gull will swallow the stolen egg on the spot; at other times it carries it back to its nest to feed to its young. On occasion biologists there have seen a gull return to its nest with an egg before its own chicks have hatched. In these cases, the incubating impulse apparently overwhelms the gull, and it drops the stolen egg intact beside its own, thus creating a puzzle for passing ornithologists who are not in the know. In the far north, gulls prey on the eggs and young of various shore birds to such an extent that one of them, the American avocet, is said by the ornithologist E. A. Armstrong to utter "a warning cry which it reserves for gulls alone."

Two species whose young suffer to some extent from gull predation are the double-crested cormorant and the common eider, yet both seem to thrive under that predation. The cormorant is a familiar figure along our coasts, perched on a buoy or an emerging rock on the falling tide, its wings hung out to dry so that it looks like a dark and scrawny armorial eagle. Western Gulls are said to have destroyed entire colonies of cormorants after human intruders had forced them to leave their nests, but under ordinary conditions the cormorants defend their nests well.

Eiders, nearly extirpated along the Atlantic coast by eggers and hunters at one time, have made a heartening comeback in recent years. Although gulls will break up an eider's nest if it is left unguarded, once again human intruders are often to blame; Tinbergen has observed that an eider, startled from its nest by a man, does not cover the eggs with its down as it is likely to if it leaves under more leisurely circumstances. In fact, while these "sea ducks" invariably establish their colonies on islands already inhabited by Herring and Great Black-backed Gulls, their numbers continue to increase to a point where biologists think they are running out of the mussels on which they prefer to feed. ("We may have an *eider* control program in Maine someday," a biologist told me, only half jokingly.)

Sometimes the eiders suffer heavy losses, it is true. But a number of biologists suggest that it may ultimately be to the eiders' advantage to breed within a gull colony. The surrounding gulls, rising to drive off marauding birds of their own or other species, inadvertently protect the eiders' nests too. The common factor in the success of both cormorants and eiders in raising their young next to predacious gulls is that they are large enough to deter persistent attacks.

Neither species, of course, deliberately sets out to nest close to gulls. The topography and vegetation of the islands, their remoteness from mammalian disturbance and their nearness to a food supply are the attractions that draw them. Similar considerations bring smaller sea birds to many of the same islands, often with disastrous results. Common

Eider-duck nest exposed

puffins nesting on level ground are known to take a bad beating from gulls on islands off Newfoundland, while those nesting on cliff edges or on slopes fare much better. Writing of the colonies of puffins and terns on Maine's Matinicus Rock, which had been the site of a gull-control program in 1971, Willaim H. Drury of the Massachusetts Audubon Society concluded:

> In 1972, the gulls were back, predation was high, the terns reproduced poorly, and few Common Puffins were evident on the Rock. It seems obvious that control of gulls on this island is necessary if the populations of other seabird species are to thrive there.

It is probable that stronger steps would have been taken against encroaching gulls long ago if they had been proved the culprits in keeping down the population of, let us say, eiders, which are valued as game birds. Since the value of puffins and terns is generally felt to be merely aesthetic, there was little clamor for their protection. In fact, suggestions by the Maine and Massachusetts Audubon societies that gull-control programs be carried out on certain islands have sometimes been vetoed by the Maine Department of Inland Fish and Game on the grounds that the control crews might dis-

15

turb the nesting eiders. But when a species interferes with human affairs, man takes action, and gulls, especially Herring Gulls, have been intruding themselves on man's notice more often of late.

In an article in *Audubon* some years ago, L. E. Dickinson showed in what curious ways gulls can do this. The Carolina Power and Light Company was once plagued by a series of temporary power failures in North Carolina. An investigation traced the trouble to the vicinity of a municipal dump. When garbage was unloaded there, flocks of gulls hovered over the area and some of them brushed both wings against the overhead transmission lines, which were energized and surrounded by a field of static electricity. Short circuits occurred regularly.

"The occasional, unlucky gulls whose wings formed a continuous path between the two wires were, of course, electrocuted," Dickinson wrote. "The problem was solved by spreading the wires farther apart, a distance exceeding the wingspread of the gulls."

Gulls cause other problems that are not so simply solved. Perhaps the most obvious is their habit of flocking to dumps in the morning and then spending the afternoon at nearby reservoirs. In the process they sometimes bring along with them parasites that are harmful to fish, or substances that may contaminate a town's water supply. Some years ago the city of Portland, Maine, strung steel wires across a city reservoir to keep out gulls "for sanitary reasons."

But certainly the most critical problem that gulls pose today is to man's flying machines. Now that man has invaded the element once dominated by birds, the two species are in conflict over the issue of *Fliegensraum*. Gulls are not, of course, the only birds implicated in plane crashes. Perhaps the most disastrous of all such encounters occurred in 1960 when an Electra's engine sucked in a flock of starlings at Boston's Logan International Airport, causing the plane to crash with the loss of sixty-two human lives. And perhaps the most bizarre incident occurred a few years ago in India, where Parsi burial towers attract clouds of vultures. A Dakota aircraft flew into the massed vultures while trying

134

to land at a nearby airport, and the copilot was killed. Subsequently the tower was moved.

But gulls are the most obvious flying hazards around airports, and their menace has increased since the introduction of high-speed jets. In a simpler era a pilot, even on landing and takeoff, might have been able to maneuver his plane to avoid the flocks of birds that strayed into his line of flight. Today the speed of commercial and military planes is so great that there is not time for either birds or planes to change direction. Moreover, the powerful jet and propjet engines sometimes, in the term used by the specialists, "ingest" birds into their openings, often with fatal results.

The Electra crash was simply one in a long list of fatal or frightening encounters. Seventeen people died at Ellicott City, Maryland, in 1962 when their plane hit two whistling swans. Two men died when a Beechcraft collided with a loon near Bakersfield, California, in 1963. The crew of a private jet fortunately escaped injury when gulls clogged an engine near Cleveland in 1968, but the expensive aircraft was demolished. Gulls were implicated in the crash of a police department helicopter at Mineola, New York, in 1974, when one man was killed and three others critically injured. And in a minor miracle, when a C-47 landed at Washington National Airport in 1963, a gull fluttered out of an engine cowling and flew away!

It is difficult to assemble accurate information about nonfatal bird strikes by aircraft, but both their number and the resulting financial loss are considerable.

"It isn't mandatory to turn in reports of these strikes," an official of the Federal Aviation Administration told me, "and naturally the commercial airlines don't like to talk about the matter for fear of upsetting their passengers. The information we get is only the tip of the iceberg. The airlines don't like to divulge their financial losses, or even how long their planes are laid up from these collisions. That might upset their stockholders. After all, it's tough to lose a half-million-dollar engine because it has sucked up a couple of birds."

Civilian aircraft suffered five hundred and thirty-seven bird strikes in one recent year, and five hundred and sixty-six in another. However, not a single commercial airline gave the FAA any estimate of the damage costs, though most of the cases involved jet engine damage due to "bird ingestion," and the airlines reported that they took many of the planes out of service for repairs.

The great majority of collisions occur at altitudes under two thousand feet, generally when the planes are landing or taking off. Military planes compound the problem because their maneuvers very often restrict them to low levels. In some years the United States Air Force reports over a thousand bird strikes, with perhaps a third of them causing "appreciable" damage to the planes. A few years ago a pilot and his crewman died when their F-101B struck a bird on takeoff and crashed in flames. The following paragraphs are part of an official Air Force report of what happened when an RF-4C collided with a black vulture at five hundred feet:

> *During low level flight, pilot saw a bird and started to warn the navigator a second prior to impact. Evasive action was not possible. The forward left edge of the pilot's canopy failed. Pilot initiated a pull-up to vacate low altitude. He was not able to see, nor could he contact the navigator due to high noise level.*
>
> *At approximately 4,000 feet he determined he was in a 70–80 degree bank. He rolled wings level and tried to contact navigator. However, the navigator, unable to see due to bird remains smeared over his visor, and unable to hear, became disoriented due to high positive "G" force of pull-up and ejected. He suffered a broken leg. Fortunately, the pilot elected to return to base and land. His parachute had been deployed by the bird strike and had separated without his knowledge.*

An FAA official provided a Cold War note. "We asked the Rus-

Fishing boats with Logan Airport in the background

sians where their military aircraft had the most trouble with birds," he recalled. "One of them grinned and said, 'At low levels, when we practice coming in low to evade the radar—just like you do.'"

The Electra crash at Boston spurred intensive research into bird problems. Although starlings caused that tragedy, gulls—because of their large size and their omnipresence at Logan Airport—became the focus of official concern. The FAA made funds available to the U.S. Fish and Wildlife Service to study the cause of bird concentrations at airports, and Fish and Wildlife in turn gave the Massachusetts Audubon Society a subcontract to carry out studies on the gulls at Logan. This brought William H. Drury, the society's research director, into the picture.

"We were fortunate that the Fish and Wildlife Service wasn't simply interested in the question of how to solve the problem," Drury told me later. "We could have documented that for them in a couple of weeks. They were also interested in the forces that combine to create a problem. That took a lot longer to answer satisfactorily, but in the process we added to our knowledge about Herring Gulls and wildlife populations in general."

Few men who have played a part in pest-control studies in this country have seen the problem as clearly as Drury did. The usual procedure is simply to ask: Is there a pest problem? If the answer is yes, the single-minded control specialists set out to eradicate the pests as soon as possible. From the very beginning, however, Drury and his colleagues saw that the solution when it came would be general and not specific. Only when man cleaned up his own sprawling mess would the problem be resolved.

Meanwhile, there were emergency measures to be considered at Logan. Seven hundred and fifty pairs of gulls had taken up nesting sites at the airport, while thousands more fed on the tidal flats and at sewer outlets nearby. From April 1960 to April 1961, observers counted thirty-eight bird strikes involving several species, including dunlins, various ducks, starlings and a snowy owl. But by far the largest number of collisions—twenty-four at least—involved gulls.

"If the architects who designed Logan had set out instead to design a gull sanctuary, they couldn't have done a better job," Drury said. "The site was surrounded by city dumps and sewer outfalls where the gulls could feed. The airport even had a dump of its own, and it was dotted with fresh water ponds and salt marshes where the gulls could loaf. Finally, it had long, isolated runways stretching into the harbor where the gulls could roost undisturbed at night. No wonder they flocked there!"

A single revealing incident confirmed Drury's notions. A small child was run down one winter day by a garbage truck driving to a city dump through a large housing project at Columbia Point in Boston. Because there had been several other traffic accidents earlier, the latest tragedy enraged the parents in the project. Defiant mothers, demanding traffic lights and other safety installations, set up barricades that prevented the trucks from driving through the project to the dump. Bill Drury and his colleagues followed the incident with great interest, noticing that the gulls, usually well fed, no longer found their meals at the dump. Almost at once they abandoned the area, flying to other parts of the coast to forage. As long as the dump remained closed, the airport's gull population sharply declined. When the Columbia Point mothers' group patched up its quarrel with the city, the gulls returned in force to their haunts at the dump and the airport.

The Massachusetts Port Authority set about making Logan less of a gulls' haven. It ordered the alluring vegetation and watering holes removed, "putting more of Logan under concrete," as one official said. The MPA also established a "gull patrol" of armed men to tour the runways regularly and frighten away the birds with exploding devices and occasional gunfire ("Just to let the birds know that we're serious"). For the most part, the patrol has carried out its duties in a professional

139

manner. Only when someone shot an osprey by mistake did Bill Drury fire off a sarcastic report.

Still, the airport authorities remain close-mouthed about the whole operation, which hardly makes for the sort of publicity the airlines relish. Chris Ayres, who took the photographs for this book, found something less than an enthusiastic reception when he asked to be admitted to the sensitive areas. On the day that he was finally permitted to accompany the gull patrol on its rounds, not a firearm was in sight. The authorities preferred to put the emphasis on a "scaregull" set up near the runways, lest anyone get the notion the menace was of such proportions that it was turning the airport into a shooting gallery.

Elsewhere, Drury had embarked on a survey of New England's Herring Gull population that is a classic of its kind. A detailed census during the 1960s indicated that there was a winter population of about seven hundred thousand Herring Gulls along the Atlantic and Gulf coasts of the United States. Most of the winter gulls were concentrated in metropolitan areas where the inevitable municipal dumps, sewer outlets and fish piers tided the birds over the cold months. Thirty-four percent of the entire East Coast population crowded into the Greater New York area. These urban centers are, of course, also the sites of the region's major airports.

Drury's counts showed one hundred and ten thousand Herring Gulls spending the winter in New England. Eighty thousand of them infested the major coastal cities; the rest foraged along less densely populated stretches of the coast, making an honest living. Drury noted that there were large breeding colonies of gulls in the Cape Cod–Vineyard Sound area during the summer, but in winter the population dropped from thirty-four thousand to eight thousand, most of them clustered around town dumps. The winter gull population at dumps and fish piers in garbage-strewn Boston Harbor was four times that of the much larger Cape Cod–Vineyard Sound region.

Drury and his colleagues also made a comprehensive survey of the summer colonies on two hundred and seventy islands from Cape May, New Jersey, near what was then the Herring Gulls' southernmost breeding limits, to eastern Maine and neighboring New Brunswick. Riding in Coast Guard planes that flew at levels below five hundred feet, they counted the gulls by sight and by taking detailed photographs of their colonies. Ground parties also counted the nests on selected islands to confirm the accuracy of the sight and photographic counts.

Drury's observers ultimately came up with a total of one hundred and thirty-five thousand breeding pairs of Herring Gulls along the northeastern coast of the United States, and another fifty thousand on nearby Canadian islands. This accounted for less than four hundred thousand birds. After taking into consideration the substantial number of winter deaths, what happened to the remaining gulls?

Drury knew that Herring Gulls do not breed until they have reached their fourth or fifth year. Among the details provided by his various counts were figures showing that a third of the winter population was made up of immature gulls still in their brown plumage. Other studies showed that each summer perhaps twenty percent of the adults "took a year off" from breeding. Again, some of the birds counted during the winter later retired to remote parts of Canada to breed.

The surveys also confirmed Drury's suspicions that earlier estimates of the average life span of adult gulls, which set it at six years, were far too low. By computing the proportion of gulls in each stage of plumage he settled on a life span closer to fifteen years. This figure accords with the facts known about the gulls' population explosion. Studies on many nesting islands during the boom years showed that although reproduction varies considerably, the total offspring reared to fledging each year averages a little better than one for each breeding pair. Those figures suggested that two hundred thousand young gulls were added to the population each summer. Only twenty-five thousand young needed to survive into their fourth year to maintain a stable population.

As Drury and his colleague Ian C. T. Nisbet point out, many of the species that man designates as "pests" have in an evolutionary sense been *selected* to be adaptable. These species are usually plants or animals occupying habitats which, as we saw with the Ring-billed Gulls, are subject to frequent modification in detail.

> *For such species, an attempt by man to suppress its population is merely another environmental change, to which it already has the capacity to adjust* [Drury and Nisbet write]. *Hunting, poisoning, and other such remedies at the point where they are "pests" can have only a very limited effect because the birds adapt and become wary. The strategy of management is then to seek the weak links in the adaptive system and to use them to make the species adjust in ways that will benefit us.*

These comments are not simply armchair theorizing. Everyone who has dealt with the "gull problem" tends to confirm them. Frank Gramlich of the U.S. Fish and Wildlife Service kills several thousand gulls a year in Maine, some of them on nesting islands, as we have seen; the remainder around cities where they cause a variety of problems at dumps and reservoirs.

"If there are two hundred gulls on a city dump and you kill all two hundred of them, there'll be two hundred more moving in the next day," Gramlich said. "And when there are mixed flocks of Herring Gulls and Black-backs, we find that we poison only the Herring Gulls. Our program is really selective for Herring Gulls, unintentionally, of course, because they are so much more agile and less suspicious at first than the Black-backs that they come in right under them and take the bait. It's like when you're trapping small mammals—you'll catch all the shrews before you start getting the mice. But the Herring Gulls are so adaptive that pretty soon they adapt to *not* taking the bait."

Man, according to Gramlich, is not nearly so adaptive. Not long ago he was called to the town of Fryeburg, Maine, where gulls were said to be a menace at the local airport. Gramlich needed only a casual glance to determine the cause of Fryeburg's problem; the town had located its new dump at the end of the airstrip.

"Move the dump," Gramlich told the town fathers.

"We can't," one of them replied. "We had a bitter argument here in town about where to put the dump. Now it would be easier to move the *airstrip*."

I had closely followed Jeremy Hatch's studies documenting the threat of the Herring Gull's spreading population to other sea birds. I had also been in touch with Bill Drury about his work on the hazards of gulls around military and civilian airports. One summer morning I joined Drury on the old lobster boat he has used for some years to visit Maine's gull colonies. The coast was blanketed in the fog for which it is notorious.

"This is really a nostalgic trip for me," Drury said as he guided the boat through the blotted-out landscape among the

16

islands in Penobscot Bay. "The federal funding for our studies has run out, but I think we learned a lot out here."

He is a tall, light-haired, youthful-looking man, a skilled boat handler and a biologist who approaches his task with imagination and wit. "There are some variables in our selection of which islands to work on," he said. "We neglected Green Island over there because it's covered with stinging nettles."

But there are many more Green Islands and Green Ledges on the Maine coast for him to choose among, because, as we have seen, greenery grows readily on islands that have been richly fertilized by gulls and is thus an indication of their presence. Often the nearby islands where gulls do not nest are comparatively drab.

Through the fog we detected Little Brimstone Island, small and treeless, on which there was a colony that Drury had been observing since 1963. It was half tide. Water foamed rhythmically over the island's lower rocks and then, still glistening white, dripped back into the surf. A dozen harbor seals had splashed off some large rocks and remained in the cove, rubbernecking at the intruders. Lobster buoys, painted bright yellow, red and green, provided the only daubs of color in this monochrome world. We anchored in twenty-five feet of water.

"Gulls are ordinarily ground nesters, so they adapted to nesting on islands where they were safe from mammalian predators," Drury said. "When the early settlers here began to take their eggs, the gulls adapted again and started building their nests in trees on some of the islands. They still build their nests in trees on Franklin Island over in Muscongus Bay."

We dropped into the lobster boat's dory and rowed ashore. A cloud of gulls rose from the ground and, shrieking, circled overhead. When we had clambered over the wet and slippery rockweed we saw the first nests with their speckled eggs just above the high-water line.

"How about your presence on the islands?" I asked Drury. "Did you find you had any effect on the birds' breeding success?"

He nodded. "There was some mortality, of course, when the parents flew off and left their eggs or chicks untended. We found that the disturbance was greater when we visited the islands only occasionally. But if we landed often the gulls got used to us, and they didn't stay away from their nests very long. There would be some mortality in cold, rainy weather when the adults weren't around to keep the eggs or chicks warm. But on the whole we felt our disturbance was small."

Some of the gulls nested in the thick vegetation that covered the crown of the island. The broken shells of sea animals studded the weedy earth. Grasses, yarrow, tansy, ragweed, angelica, silverweed and mouse-eared chickweed formed most of the cover. Nearby on the rocks we saw dozens of gulls' nests. Often there were dim splotches of paint on the rocks beside a nest.

"We used to come to the island in June and count the nests," Drury said. "Then we'd make a mark next to each one—a splash of green paint meant there were eggs in the nest, blue paint meant no eggs. On some of the rocks you can see a number of marks, one for each year there was a nest on that spot. It helped us keep track of the nests we'd already counted, and it gave us an idea of nesting sites and how successful they were from year to year."

"Do gulls make good parents?"

Drury grinned. "Gulls are like people. Some are good parents, some are lousy ones. Gulls have excellent hatching success with their eggs—sometimes as high as eighty percent. But many of the chicks die before fledging, as you know, most of them during the first five days of their lives. We found that the main reason for this is that many of the parents just don't make the transition in time from incubating eggs to feeding and caring for their young. So the young die from neglect."

We ate our sandwiches on the rocks without walking up into the tall weeds high on the island. Common eiders nested there, and Drury did not want to disturb them. Below us on the glassy black swell, clusters of eider chicks swam behind the adults. A few Great Black-backed

Gulls stood about on the distant rocks, apparently waiting for something to turn up.

They did not have long to wait. Eider chicks, being truly precocial birds, move into the water almost as soon as they hatch, and they are fed there by their mother. We saw a hen eider, a large brown bird barred with darker lines, emerge from the weeds and start for the shore with her five chicks waddling furiously behind her. A cruising Black-back swooped on the group and the duck turned, rising to meet the attacker with flailing wings. The gull passed overhead and the convoy resumed its dash for the water. But several other Black-backs had noticed the commotion. Two, then three swept in. The duck turned threateningly on them, then waddled on, the chicks tumbling over the rocks and seaweed in her wake. Not all of them made it. Two gulls were successful, swooping to pluck scurrying chicks from the group just as they reached the water. The great bird's bill obscured the chick; there was only a leg kicking feebly from one corner before disappearing entirely. Three of the chicks swam off with their mother.

What happens to the young gulls when, after two months of varying parental care, they are ready to leave the island? Do they fare any better than the eiders? Drury, drawing on his own research and that of others, is able to supply a few of the answers. About a third of the fledged birds die during the first month while they are learning to fend for themselves. A few follow the adults to feeding areas along the coast, begging food from them or finding out what to search for on their own.

"Fledged birds, like nestlings, inherit certain patterns of behavior such as searching, probing, diving, prying and so forth," Drury said. "But they have to learn what to search for and what to eat."

As Bill Drury and I talked about the first few months of a gull's life, those months when its chances for survival are meager, I recalled long, lazy afternoons in late summer when I had watched a part of that desperate struggle for food. Groups of Herring Gulls gather to feed at low water on the mudflats in front of the cabin where I write. In late

Immature gull

August or early September these groups are likely to include chicks which have only recently left the colony where they hatched, perhaps, in this case, the Green Island that neighbors Petit Manan. The drab brown chicks follow the adults, often apparently their parents, to nearby feeding areas, counting on the adults' waning interest in them to revive sufficiently to provide a few more meals.

One afternoon in early September was typical. The tide was going out. As the water level dropped, it began to float the tops of rockweed on its ruffled surface in patches of undulant bronze. Widening expanses of mudflat were bared. My attention was drawn to those mudflats by a thin, high-pitched whistle, repeated over and over, like the mildly irritating notes produced by a small boy learning to use a bosun's pipe. An immature gull stood in the mud next to an adult. It was curiously hunched, its feathers ruffled, its neck drawn in, as though it had done something it shouldn't have and expected to be slapped down for it. Hunched, uttering its high, two syllabled note *(peeyee)*, it approached the adult, begging to be fed.

On previous occasions I had seen an adult gull attack and drive away a young bird approaching it in this posture; the unfortunate chick in those cases probably had not been able to find its parent and had presumed to beg from a stranger. On this afternoon the adult gull seemed indifferent but not intolerant. The chick kept thrusting its bill up to the adult's, nuzzling it, sometimes grasping it. The adult did its best to ignore the begging chick, turning away or stepping aside, but betraying no irritation. I was impressed by its patience. The incessant pleading note, the constant advances, would have tried Job himself.

Nearby, a great blue heron fed in a rocky pool. It was the soul of stateliness, taking one measured step after another: lifting a foot from the water, toes gathered like a bunch of bananas, pushing the leg slowly ahead, toes spreading again, planting the foot softly back in the water with scarcely a ripple; then taking another step. The heron's arched neck suddenly uncoiled, propelled the long rapier bill into the pool and seized a tiny silver fish. The heron chomped once and swallowed. Then it shook its head deliberately, carefully, as if the great burden of its bill might carry the head away if it were shaken too vigorously.

The heron appeared to be absolutely imperturbable. But the two gulls had ventured into the pool where it fed, the chick increasingly insistent, its pleading cry now almost unbearable. It kept thrusting its bill up to the adult's as if it were crossing swords. The adult turned and strode away, the crouching chick in frantic pursuit. The heron had suffered enough of the intrusion. It made a run at the two gulls, sending them scurrying apart. The chick stood on a rock, looking bewildered for a moment, then resumed its pursuit of the parent. At last the adult gull stopped, stretched its neck, heaved and brought up a lumpy puddle of food. The chick consumed it instantly. When it turned to the adult again, the older gull flew away.

I told Drury of the encounter. Would "my" gull survive? Its chances were probably better than most, Drury thought. It had obviously found a parent on the feeding grounds, and the occasional meal it was able to beg would help to tide it over until it learned to recognize food apart from the scrambled meal an adult regurgitated at its feet.

"But there are other factors involved besides finding a parent after they've left the colony," Drury said. "We've learned that the chicks which hatch early have a better chance than those which hatch later on. Perhaps they establish dominance over the younger chicks. This can be a big advantage if food is scarce in the fall and winter. A chick must be aggressive if it isn't going to starve. In fact, we've found that young gulls are bolder than adults when it comes to rushing in and grabbing food when threatening adults are around—as long as it isn't in the feeding territory of the adult. I guess you can say that they're more desperate."

After the breeding season the adult gulls fly away from the colony and take up their natural feeding areas along the shore. It is difficult for a chick to break into these. If it cannot find a parent, it will probably be driven away. The chicks wander more as the fall progresses, flying farther south than the adults do (New England chicks drift south of New Jersey for the winter, while the adults may move only a hundred miles or so south of where they nested). And the creation of artificial feeding areas by man—dumps, sewer outlets, fish canneries and other manifestations of man's sloppiness—allow Herring Gull chicks to survive in "unnatural" numbers and swell the species' population.

Man, who accelerates the process of extinction, is also the creator of animal pests.

What is the situation between man and gull today? Tentative steps have been taken to clean up the most obvious sources of trouble. Cities have converted a few dumps to sanitary landfills (though some gulls continue to visit the sites), and the federal government has allocated a little money to help municipalities move dumps away from critical areas. An Inter-Agency Bird Committee now functions within the federal government, encouraging research to deal with the threat to military and civilian aircraft.

Improvements in aircraft design have already helped to

17

some extent. Jet engines are placed higher on many of the newer planes, causing some experts to conjecture that they no longer suck up as many birds (or even rocks and rabbits) from runways as they used to. Experiments are going on at U.S. Air Force laboratories to see if white strobe lights will be useful at long range in warning birds off a plane's course.

Whatever figures are available, however, indicate that the damage to both military and civilian planes increased during the early 1970s. Federal and local authorities have yet to use the leverage they obtained after the Electra crash at Boston. In sustaining claims for death and injury against the federal government, a U.S. district court held that the authorities were negligent in failing to force the removal of "attractions to birds" near the airport. A section of the Federal Airport Grant Act reads:

> *Airport hazard means any structure or object of natural growth located on or in the vicinity of a public airport, or any use of land near such airport, which obstructs the air force required for the flight of aircraft in landing or taking off at such airport or is otherwise hazardous to such landing or taking off of aircraft.*

The gulls' depredations among the eggs and chicks of other species remain severe. An indirect effect of the gulls' monopoly on many islands that harbor birds was shown at Gardiners Island off Long Island, where the remnants of a once-flourishing common-tern colony were pushed during the early 1970s farther and farther to a marginal site at the northern end of the island. In 1972 Hurricane Agnes sent the sea thundering across that exposed point, wiping out the tern colony. The terns did not try to re-nest the following year.

"Why not declare an open season on gulls?" someone always asks after a discussion of gull problems. The answer, in practical terms, is that shooting the birds would serve to make them wary, without solving the problem. A few gulls would be shot, but others would move into the critical area. Moreover, conservationists have struggled too long for sound bird-protection laws to surrender any gains at this point. Many hunters do not know one species of game bird from another at any distance and, with little experience, they would be even less likely to distinguish a Herring Gull or a Western Gull from rarer gulls or terns and other sea birds. At present, gull problems are social, not biological.

Bill Drury and Ian Nisbet advocate tackling the problem locally in an emergency, driving gulls off those islands where their presence poses an immediate threat to aircraft or the survival of other sea-bird colonies. "A control program which involves eliminating gulls [locally] is an unpalatable prospect," Nisbet writes, "but the situation itself is unpalatable."

Meanwhile, Drury's latest counts and computations reveal that the Herring Gulls' breeding population has ended its upward spiral in the Northeast. The evidence suggests that these gulls are not producing as many young as they did a few years ago, and also that they may have reached the limits of the available food and nesting space in that part of the country. The competition for both food and land may be intense; certainly there are more nonbreeding adults now than there were a few years ago, a fact noted by Frank Gramlich when gulls he has "controlled" on islands where they breed are immediately replaced by others moving into the vacuum.

It seems clear that there is a direct correlation between the breeding success of Herring Gulls and man's domestic and industrial garbage. The New England fishing industry, plagued by its antiquated equipment and the insatiable foreign fleets offshore, is on the verge of collapse. Fish offal is no longer available to gulls in unlimited quantities during their breeding season. Perhaps, too, a subtle and unanalyzed difference in the composition of garbage at municipal dumps recently has affected the gulls to some extent. ("The poisonous refuse they eat at dumps would kill a regiment," Gramlich observes.)

Even if the hungry adult gulls are inclined to breed, they cannot sustain a large production of young. The closing of dumps here and there also seems to have caused local winter die-offs. Drury believes that during the next decade we may see, admittedly on a smaller scale, a repetition of the movement away from the crowded Maine colonies into Massachusetts that took place during the 1940s.

Many gulls winter in southern New England and the opportunity to settle and breed on islands with which they were already familiar may have been a factor in the rapid growth of the breeding gull population in southern New England [Drury and John A. Kadlec, a government biologist, wrote in 1974]. Relatively few adult Herring Gulls winter south of New Jersey, so that there is less advantage from familiarity gained during the winter. Nevertheless our present observations on the state of the Herring Gull population suggest that it will be prudent to look for growth of gull colonies in the middle and south Atlantic states in the next decade. If such proves to be the case, we would anticipate an increase of gulls at and around the many commercial and military airports in the South.

Their words have already assumed a prophetic ring. Both Herring Gulls and Great Black-backed Gulls are gradually spreading their ranges south. For a time the Herring Gulls' most southerly breeding colony was at Stone Harbor, New Jersey. In 1955 they bred in Maryland on Chesapeake Bay, and in 1958 at Chinctateague, Virginia. In 1962 Jack Hailman and his wife, while studying a large Laughing Gull colony in Pamlico Sound, North Carolina, fifteen miles north of Cape Hatteras, found Herring Gulls nesting there (one egg hatched). In 1971, biologists found these gulls nesting, mostly on man-made dredge islands, at various points along the North Carolina coast as far south as the Cape Fear River. Great Black-backed Gulls, whose most southerly nesting site

Gulls waiting for bulldozer to turn over garbage

was at Jamaica Bay, New York City, in 1967, have followed the Herring Gulls into North Carolina.

The outpost colonies are thriving, biologists say. In an article in *The Auk,* the Journal of the American Ornithologists' Union, in 1975, James F. Parnell and Robert F. Soots wrote that the spread of the large gulls southward "may have ominous ecological significance," and cited evidence that they have been preying on chicks of the royal tern which nests in North Carolina. The terns abandoned a colony that had suffered "considerable mortality," apparently from gulls.

Juvenile and nonbreeding adults are being seen in South Carolina with increasing frequency during recent summers, an indication that it is only a matter of time before nests will be found. In a study made of air strikes at the Charleston Air Force Base, biologists determined that the numbers of Herring and Ring-billed Gulls there had increased during the past fifteen years and now posed the chief hazards to planes. They were feeding at eight dumps and landfills inland and were joined on airfields, mostly during rainy, windy weather, by Laughing Gulls which depended for food on the shrimp trawlers just offshore.

As the residues of industrial civilization insinuate themselves more and more thoroughly along the southerly extensions of our coastlines, East and West, there will be adaptable creatures on hand to take advantage of the altered landscape. Gulls, as we have observed, have the capacity to deal with abrupt changes. We are free to make those changes, but it will be better for us in the future if we are aware of all the ripples that our actions send out across the face of the planet.

Gulls are adaptable enough so that their relationship with us is not, as it is for so many other animals, completely lopsided in humanity's favor. Gulls, we might also remember, would survive without man's presence, as they did for untold centuries. It is not demeaning our own species to say that despite our handouts to them, we would be poorer without gulls than they would be without us; these beautiful and fascinating creatures add to the marvelous natural diversity that enriches our lives.

Ideally, we ought to be able to see them in the context

Epilogue

of their world as it was before we intruded. The gull colonies, first decimated and then inflated by human interference, are still the places
where gulls, interacting with their own and other species, behave pretty
much as they always have. On Kent Island, New Brunswick, there is
perhaps the largest breeding colony of Herring Gulls in North America.
Although its inhabitants are sustained in part by the wastes of Canadian
fishermen, the area is so large that a human visitor receives the rare impression of being a part, and not the ruler, of another species' world.

I arrived on Kent Island in the middle of June, traveling by ferry
from the mainland to Grand Manan and the rest of the way by a lobster boat that belongs to the island's caretaker. Kent is the largest of a
cluster of three islands at the southern extremity of the Grand Manan
archipelago, rising amid the swift currents and enormous tides of the
Bay of Fundy. It is a long, narrow body of land, a mile and three
quarters from tip to tip and comprising a little over two hundred acres
of meadow, rocks and forest.

Although Kent Island lies within the province of New Brunswick,
the nearest point on the mainland is Cutler, Maine, fifteen miles away,
and the island itself is owned by Bowdoin College. For much of the
year Kent is inhabited only by a large colony of muskrats. But in the
late spring transients of all sorts arrive, including many kinds of birds to
establish their nesting sites and a small number of biologists and students
to pursue their research. The Bowdoin College Scientific Station has
maintained several old buildings there since 1934, when J. Sterling
Rockefeller bought the island and gave it to the college. For the most
part, the seventeen thousand pairs of Herring Gulls (and a few Great
Black-backed Gulls) which nest on Kent Island do the best they can to
ignore the presence of the scientists, and in turn the scientists, the majority of whom have come to the island to study other species, adopt a
similar aloofness; one may admire the beauty of a dozen gulls, or even a
hundred, but thirty-odd thousand blaring neighbors sometimes inspire
other emotions.

Herring Gull nesting island

Yet their very density on and over the island established the gulls in my mind as a "nation." They came here in multitudes, strong in their nationhood, indomitable in their common impulse to produce and rear a new generation, and admiration was irrelevant. In their multitudes, as I watched, I was able to detect individuality, too. Every morning I walked to the southern end of the island, where the gulls nested in the open on rocks and peaty earth. Once they had grown accustomed to my presence, and if I did not come too close to their nests, they carried on as if I were merely another gutted stump in the landscape. Some hundred yards away, a dozen or more gulls wheeled in leisurely flight, but one of them was agitated, beating its wings so ardently among its indolent companions that it looked like another species. Standing on a rock, indifferent but no doubt alert to my presence, was another gull with a curiously deformed bill, twisted and fluted, shaped almost like a corkscrew. Increasingly during the last few years biologists have noted deformities among several species of sea birds on breeding colonies, notably terns. (On a Long Island Sound colony a tern chick was found with four legs, others with abnormally small eyes, others without down or flight feathers.) The biologists attribute many of these deformities to the contamination of surrounding waters by pesticides or related chemicals. But for all of this gull's oddity, it was mature and apparently prospering, its misshapen bill no hindrance to its ability to feed itself.

An incubating gull nearby would have warmed the heart of any inveterate bumbler. The gull and its mate had built their nest in a shallow cavern which extended a foot or so into the sharply inclined peaty hillside. The choice of the location seemed to me, as it must have to the gulls, especially felicitous, for the soft earth was easy to mold into a depression and the overhang gave the birds some protection from the rain and the noon sun. The trouble was that the cavern had very little overhead room. When sitting on the nest, the gull had to crane its neck sideways, like an engineer sticking his head out the window of his locomotive.

For the most part, the gulls lived on peaceful terms with one another, now that the territorial squabbles were settled and they had turned to incubating their eggs. But one day I saw a rousing battle. It seemed to have started with one gull invading the territory of another at the top of a slope, and by the time I focused my binoculars on the scene, blood was smeared over the heads and chests of both birds, so that they looked like a couple of heavyweight boxers. They clung to each other's bills and grappled fiercely. I could see a wound at the base of one gull's bill, so perhaps it had shed all of the blood. The two combatants, still grappling, disappeared from my view over the brow of the hill before they had come to a decision.

I saw very few chicks when I arrived, but in a day or two they began to hatch. Walking across the rocks late in the afternoon of June 24, I noticed a nest with three eggs in it. The adult was especially agitated by my approach, rising on frantically flapping wings, then swooping with a grating *kek-kek-kek* and sometimes brushing my head with its dangling feet. I stopped momentarily for a close look and then passed on hurriedly; a damp chick was nearly out of one of the eggs, wriggling feebly to free itself, another had just pecked open its tiny window on the world, the third egg was intact. I returned to the nest the next morning. The eldest chick was now a fluffy, alert little being, while the second had just emerged from the shell, prone and stupefied by its effort, its bill resting on the rim of the nest. The third egg was still unpipped. The following morning, June 26, both chicks were dry and fluffy, the egg unpipped. When I passed the nest on June 27 at nine in the morning, all three chicks were dry, fluffy and vigorous on the nest. The adults had brought forth a full complement, though the chances were that only one chick would be alive a year later. In order not to increase the odds against them any further, I did not visit the nest again.

Wherever I walked and looked, the gulls had put their imprint on the island. Although their webbed feet are adapted for swimming or for padding around on the rocks, they displayed remarkable agility in landing on trees, keeping their balance on slender branches or broken stubs. Sometimes a dozen gulls perched in a single tree. Their weight had apparently deformed many of Kent Island's spruces, dwarfing them and leveling their tops, so that clusters of trees sometimes resembled a bonsai grove. There were many dead trees, too, some of them killed by the guano lavished on them by roosting gulls.

The rocks were whitewashed, and occasionally splotched in bright pinks and purples, pigments taken from the mussels or other sea creatures eaten by the gulls and passed through the alimentary tract. On other rocks there were curious little packets of shell and gristle, cemented into compact ovals. On pulling them apart, I found they were the pellets of indigestible material regurgitated by gulls, like the balls of hair and bone coughed up by a cat after it has eaten a mouse.

The gulls do not live alone on the island, not by thousands. There are the biologists and the muskrats (several times I first mistook young of the latter, scurrying unseen through the undergrowth, for gull chicks). There are Savannah sparrows. There are hundreds of tree swallows, many of them nesting in boxes erected by the biologists. There are black guillemots nesting in crevices in the rocks, carrying on in the midst of the gulls, uttering their faint tinkling notes, spreading their stubby wings to show off the big white patches.

Common eiders nest in profusion on Kent Island too. Their nests are generally hidden in high grass or in the forest, sometimes on the shore under sheltering fragments of driftwood. Two of the Bowdoin students were following the movements of the eiders that successfully convoyed their young through the gauntlet of predacious gulls to the water. As soon as they reached the water, many began swimming with their chicks in tow toward Grand Manan. Although eiders do not nest on that larger island, hundreds of ducks and their young can be seen offshore. The fish canneries on Grand Manan, it seems, are a more attractive source of food for gulls than are eider chicks.

What else lives in the gulls' world on Kent Island? Something,

Gulls fighting in the air

perhaps, beyond our knowledge. Early one evening as we were preparing for dinner at the scientific station, a student uttered a whoop and rushed outside. The rest of us followed to see what had caught his attention through the window. It was one of the most spectacular displays I have ever witnessed. A moment earlier the island had been wrapped in comparative quiet. Then it erupted in a welter of screaming, circling gulls. The eruption apparently began at the southern end of the island. The birds there rose from their nests in a "panic flight." The panic swept like a great wave of anxiety up the island, so that within a few moments the air was clogged with over thirty thousand gulls. They came swirling up from the ragwort and sheep sorrel to the south, then from the raspberries and grasses in the center of the island, and finally from the dense forest at the northern end.

What had stirred this panic? Two of the students climbed to the tower on top of the main building, thinking that an eagle had suddenly appeared over the island, but nothing was in sight, though the students scanned the horizon. There was no eagle, no boat carrying gunners or sightseers, no climatic disturbance that might have touched some common chord of fear within the thousands of birds. Such "panic flights" are sometimes observed within tern colonies too, and go largely unexplained. In this case, the blizzard of birds subsided as quickly as it began. The gulls settled back onto their nests, though for a long time afterward a low chatter of excitement could be heard coming from the colony.

Almost as shadowy as panic is the great subterranean colony of birds that shares Kent Island with the gulls. It is a city of night, a vibrant mass of small creatures called Leach's storm-petrels, sooty-plumaged, catbird-sized sea birds which inhabit burrows in the honeycombed earth beneath the gulls' nests in the forest on the northern part of the island. Dr. Charles E. Huntington, the scientific station's director, has been coming to Kent for many years to study them.

These petrels are occasionally seen by day far out at sea, dark motes glancing off the obsidian slopes of waves, but not on the island.

They come and go only by night. Fluttery, batlike fliers, they would be easy prey for gulls as they made their way to their burrows in daylight. Perhaps as many as fifteen thousand pairs of petrels come to the island to dig out their nests among the growth of raspberries and asters under the dense stand of lichen-draped spruces, working with their tiny webbed feet and their curious black beaks, ridged with tubed nostrils. The petrels return year after year to the same burrows. There, an arm's length down its earthen tunnel, the female lays a single white egg. The parents take turns—one brooding the egg in the dark while the other forages over the sea, waiting until night to return and change places with its mate.

Chuck Huntington, who bands them, finds that some of the petrels are at least twenty-five years old. One banded as a nestling in 1963 returned as an adult in 1967 to dig a burrow less than four feet away from that of its parents; and several years later it took possession of the burrow where it had hatched. Huntington's banded petrels have been found as far away as the eastern Atlantic Ocean off Spain and West Africa.

One night I followed Huntington into the midst of this shadowy life, this other side of the coin from the gulls' tumultuous daylight world. We walked in tingling silence along a path through the trees. There was a large gibbous moon in a cloudless sky. Occasionally our footsteps sent a roosting gull flapping in confusion out of the high branches.

The moonlight fell on the forest, where its shafts were sorted out and fractured, their fragments scattered through the dark foliage to glint and twinkle like tinsel. The spruce trees basked in dappled radiance. The tips of some grew incandescent; others lingered in gloom, ghostly, fragrant, tangible particles of night itself. As we pushed through the glinting branches I half expected to hear the popping of tiny light bulbs. But the moonshafts simply dropped through the fleeting openings to strike fire from a lower level.

167

The air around us was in a flutter, alive with shadowy winged things silhouetted against the radiance. Petrels were coming in from the sea, threading their way through the trees to their burrows. In flight they uttered a sweet twitter, a thin burst of sound spiraling down into silence. The forest canopy grew denser. I sniffed at the shadows, which smelled of guano and rotting vegetation. Occasionally Huntington flashed his light ahead of us, hollowing out the darkness for a few feet, but compressing its farther walls into impenetrable gloom.

"We're in the colony," he whispered. "Listen."

From the porous floor of the island forest came a sound that few human beings have heard. It was a melodious purring, pulsing yet sustained, a song crooned in the subterranean blackness by petrels to their mates during those intervals when they were both at the nest. Other petrels, perhaps guided by the song and the musky odor peculiar to the family of petrels and albatrosses, were dropping like inky scraps from the night sky to locate their own burrows among the thousands that lie under the forest litter. To these creatures, the lives of men are as alien, as utterly unknown, as the lives of gulls. Not even that tremulous music from the burrows, and our own good will, can bridge the enormous gulf between our two kinds of life.

The next morning I was back in the world of gulls and men. It was not a world to spin fanciful dreams about, for the ugliness and harshness glared through the beauty, while the lives of petrels seemed as dim and remote to me as the age of Atlantis. The morning air was full of gulls' cries. The sea, pallid under a dissolving fog, stirred in smooth, languid mounds. Clusters of gulls rested buoyantly on the water around the island. As I watched them I was reminded of Oliver Wendell Holmes's phrase "The gull, high floating like a sloop unladen."

Soon the birds would be leaving Kent Island. The chicks that survived the hazards of the colony would go streaming down the coastline in search of food, wandering for several years until their mottled brown plumage blossomed to nuptial white and they returned here to produce their new generations.

The gull has far more in common with us than the petrel does. We are contemporaries in a sense, riding the runaway vehicle that is the modern industrial world. In life and literature the gull has had many human admirers. Now our own shortcomings have brought us into a degrading conflict with this beautiful and resourceful creature. If the bald eagle is the symbol of our country's grandeur, the Herring Gull may come to stand for something far less noble in our national character.

Bibliographical Notes

PAGE

Chapter 1

13-14 Ernest Hart, Jr., "Several hundred ways of looking at a seagull." *The Fiddlehead,* No. 93 (Spring 1972).

17 Henry Beston, *The Outermost House.* New York, 1928.

18-19 Orson F. Whitney, *History of Utah.* New York, 1892.

19-20 W. H. Hudson, *The Land's End.* New York, 1927.

Chapter 2

22 Gerald A. Sanger, "Pelagic records of Glaucous-winged and Herring Gulls in the North Pacific Ocean." *Auk,* 90:384-393 (1973).

22 Dean Amadon, *Birds Around the World.* New York, 1966.

23 James Fisher and Roger Tory Peterson, *World of Birds.* Garden City, N.Y., 1964.

24-26 M. Moynihan, "California Gulls and Herring Gulls breeding in the same colony." *Auk,* 73:453-454 (1956).

26-28 Neal Griffith Smith, *Evolution of Some Arctic Gulls* (Larus): *An Experimental Study of Isolating Mechanisms.* Ornithological Monographs, No. 4. American Ornithologists' Union, 1966.

Chapter 3

30 O. S. Pettingill, "An 'ancient' Herring Gull." *Eastern Bird Banding News,* 30:180 (1967).

30 George M. Jonkel and O. S. Pettingill, "Retraction of a longevity record for a 36-year-old Herring Gull." *Auk,* 91:432 (1974).

PAGE

30 A. Landsborough Thomson, *A New Dictionary of Birds.* New York, 1964.

31 A. D. Walker, "New light on the origins of birds and crocodiles." *Nature,* 237:257-263 (1972).

31 W. T. Neill, *The Ruling Reptiles.* New York, 1971.

31 Joel Carl Welty, *The Life of Birds.* Philadelphia, 1962.

31 Josselyn Van Tyne and Andrew J. Berger, *Fundamentals of Ornithology.* New York, 1959.

31 N. P. Ashmole, "The biology of the wideawake or Sooty Tern *Sterna fuscata* on Ascension Island." *Ibis,* 103b:297-364 (1963).

32 Peter Matthiessen, *The Wind Birds.* New York, 1973.

32 Niko Tinbergen, *The Herring Gull's World.* London, 1953.

32 Irston R. Barnes, in *The Wood Thrush* [formerly the publication of the Audubon Naturalist Society of the Central Atlantic States] (September, 1946).

34 Edwin Way Teale, *Autumn Across America.* New York, 1956.

34 A. H. Woodcock, "Observations on Herring Gull soaring." *Auk,* 57:219-224 (1940).

34 Welty, *Life of Birds.*

34 A. H. Woodcock, "Soaring over the open sea." *Sci. Monthly,* 55:226-232 (1942).

35 John James Audubon, *Journals.* London, 1908.

36 Niko Tinbergen, "Clever gulls and dumb ethologists." *Vogelwarte,* 26:232-238 (1971).

36 *International Wildlife Encyclopedia,* Vol. 8. New York, 1969.

36 H. Brackbill, "Fowl that don't befoul." *Maryland Conservationist,* 48:4–7 (1972).

37 Clarence Cottam, "California Gulls feeding on midges." *Condor,* 47:216 (1945).

37 A. C. Bent, *Life Histories of North American Gulls and Terns.* U.S. Natl. Mus. Bull. 133 (1921).

37 Clarence Cottam, "Gulls as vegetarians." *Condor,* 46:127–128 (1944).

37 Van Tyne and Berger, *Fundamentals.*

37 Tinbergen, *Herring Gull's World.*

37 L. Ph. Bolander, "A robin roost in Oakland, California." *Condor,* 34:142–143 (1932).

37–38 Jack P. Hailman, "Why is the Galápagos Gull the color of lava?" *Condor,* 65:528 (1963).

38 Van Tyne and Berger, *Fundamentals.*

Chapter 4

42 William H. Drury and I. C. T. Nisbet, "The importance of movements in the biology of Herring Gulls in New England." *Wildlife Research Report 2.* U.S. Department of the Interior (1972).

43 *International Wildlife Encyclopedia,* Vol. 2. New York, 1969.

43–44 Herbert K. Job, cited in Bent, *Life Histories.*

44 John Bull, *Birds of the New York Area.* New York, 1964.

44–45 David Saunders, *Sea Birds.* New York, 1973.

45–46 Jack P. Hailman, "Strange gull of the Galápagos." *Audubon,* 68: 180–184 (1966).

46 ———, "The Galápagos Swallow-tailed Gull is nocturnal." *Wilson Bull.,* 76:347–354 (1964).

46 ———, "Cliff-nesting adaptations of the Galápagos Swallow-tailed

Gull." *Wilson Bull.,* 77:346–362 (1965).

48 *American Birds,* 28:612 (1974).

48 Edward Burtt, Jr., "Success of two feeding methods of the Black-legged Kittiwake." *Auk,* 91: 827–829 (1974).

49–50 Bent, *Life Histories.*

50–51 E. Cullen, "Adaptations in the Kittiwake to cliff-nesting." *Ibis,* 99:275–302 (1957).

51–52 Saunders, *Sea Birds.*

52 *International Wildlife Encyclopedia,* Vol. 9. New York, 1969.

Chapter 5

54 Niko Tinbergen, *The Animal in Its World,* Vol. I. Cambridge, Mass., 1972.

55 Tinbergen, *Herring Gull's World.*

56 M. H. MacRoberts, "Extramarital courting in Lesser Black-backed Gulls and Herring Gulls." *Tierpsychol.,* 32:62–74. (1973).

56 Van Tyne and Berger, *Fundamentals.*

56 James Fisher and R. M. Lockley, *The Herring Gull and Its Egg.* Leiden, 1970.

56–58 William Threllfall, et al., "Seabird mortality in a storm." *Auk,* 91:846–849 (1974).

58 Bent, *Life Histories.*

58 Joanna Burger, "Breeding biology and ecology of the Brown-hooded Gull in Argentina." *Auk,* 91:601–613 (1974).

58 Tinbergen, *The Animal in Its World.*

58 Amadon, *Birds Around the World.*

60 Niko Tinbergen, "The Shell Menace." *Natural History,* 72:28–35 (1963).

60 Tinbergen, *The Animal in Its World.*

61 Jack P. Hailman, *The Ontogeny of an Instinct.* Leiden, 1967.

61 ———, "How an instinct is

formed." *Scientific American,*
221:98–106 (1969).

61 J. T. Emlen, "Juvenile mortality in
a Ring-billed Gull colony."
Wilson Bull., 68:232–238 (1956).

62 E. H. Forbush and J. B. May,
*Natural History of the Birds of
Eastern and Central North America.*
Boston, 1939.

Chapter 6

64 Peter Matthiessen. *Widlife in
America.* New York, 1959.

64 Frank Graham, Jr., *Man's Dominion:
The Story of Conservation in
America.* New York, 1971.

65 Ralph S. Palmer, *Maine Birds.*
Cambridge, Mass., 1949.

66 Oliver S. Austin, Jr., *Birds of thel
World.* New York, 1961.

66–68 Robert Henry Welker, *Birds and
Men.* Cambridge, Mass., 1955.

Chapter 7

70 H. Kruuk, *Predators and Anti-
Predation Behavior of the Black-
headed Gull* (Larus ridibundus).
Leiden, 1964.

70 Bent, *Life Histories.*

72–74 Graham, *Man's Dominion.*

74–75 James B. Trefethen, *Crusade for
Wildlife.* Harrisburg, Pa., 1961.

78 W. H. Hudson, *Birds and Man.*
New York, 1923.

80 David Wetherbee, et al., *Time
Lapse Ecology, Muskeget Island,
Nantucket, Massachusetts.* New
York, 1972.

Note: Much of this chapter is based
on material, letters and publications
in the files of the National Audubon Society, New York, N.Y., and
the Massachusetts Audubon Society,
Lincoln, Mass.

Chapters 8 and 9—see note above.

Chapter 10

95 ff. Jeremy J. Hatch, "Predation and
piracy by gulls at a ternery in
Maine." *Auk,* 87:244–254 (1970).

Chapter 11

102 Aldo Leopold, *A Sand County
Almanac.* New York, 1949.

102 Alison Rand Carleton and Oscar
T. Owre, "The Red-whiskered
Bulbul in Florida, 1960–71."
Auk, 92:40–57 (1975).

103 Frank Graham, Jr., "Bye-bye blackbirds?" *Audubon* 73 (No. 5):28–
35 (September 1971).

106 Arthur Rubinstein, *My Young
Years.* New York, 1973.

106–8 Audubon, *Journals.*

108 Bull, *Birds of the New York Area.*

108 William H. Drury, "Population
changes in New England sea-
birds." Parts 1 and 2. *Bird-
Banding,* 44:267–313 (1973) and
45:1–15 (1974).

108–10 Bent, *Life Histories.*

110 David F. Costello, *The World of the
Gull.* New York, 1969.

110 *International Wildlife Encyclopedia,*
Vol. 2. New York, 1969.

110 Austin, *Birds of the World.*

Chapter 12

111 Forbush and May, *Birds of Eastern
and Central North America.*

112 Alfred O. Gross, in *Acta XI Con-
gressus Internationalis Ornithologici.*
Basel, 1954.

114 E. M. Crowell and Sears Crowell,
"The displacement of terns by
Herring Gulls at the Weepecket
Islands." *Bird-Banding,* 17:1–10
(1946).

114 Drury, "Population changes."

114 Marsden Hartley, *Androscoggin.*
Portland, Me., 1940.

116 Palmer, *Maine Birds.*
117 Forbush and May, *Birds of Eastern and Central North America.*
117 Alfred O. Gross, "The Herring Gull-Cormorant control project 1944-1952." Unpublished. In Bowdoin College Library, Brunswick, Me.
118 Palmer, *Maine Birds.*
118-19 Alfred O. Gross, *Autobiography.* Unpublished. In Bowdoin College Library, Brunswick, Me.

Chapter 13

121 Julian Huxley, *Memories.* New York, 1970.
122 C. M. Herman and Gordon Bolander, "Fungus diseases in a Glaucous-winged Gull." *Condor,* 45:160-161 (1943).
122 W. A. Davis and L. S. McClung, "Aspergillosis in wild Herring Gulls." *Journ. of Bacteriology,* 40:321-323 (1940).
122 Neill, *Ruling Reptiles.*
122 L. J. Blus, et al., "Logarithmic relationship of DDE residues to eggshell thinning." *Nature,* 235: 376-377 (1972).
122 J. A. Bogan and W. R. P. Bourne, "Organochlorine levels in Atlantic seabirds." *Nature,* 240:358 (1972).
122 J. A. Keith, "Reproduction in a colony of Herring Gulls." *J. Appl. Ecol.,* 3 (Suppl.):57-70 (1966).
122 ff. James P. Ludwig, "Recent changes in the Ring-billed Gull population and biology in the Laurentian Great Lakes." *Auk,* 91:575-594 (1974).

Chapter 14

128 Kruuk, *Predators.*
128-29 A. C. Twomay, "California Gulls and exotic eggs." *Condor,* 50: 97-100 (1948).

129 E. A. Armstrong, *Bird Life.* New York, 1950.
130 Bent, *Life Histories.*
130 Drury, "Population changes."
130 Tinbergen, *Herring Gull's World.*
132 D. N. Nettleship, "Breeding success of the Common Puffin *(Fratercula arctica* L.) on different habitats at Great Island, Newfoundland." *Ecol. Monogr.,* 42: 239-268 (1972).
132 Drury, "Population changes."

Chapter 15

134 L. E. Dickinson, "Utilities and birds." *Audubon,* 59:54-55 (1957).
134 Palmer, *Maine Birds.*
134 William H. Drury, "Results of a study of Herring Gull populations and movements in southeastern New England." Colloque: Le Problème des Oiseaux sur les Aérodromes. Inst. Nat. Rech. Agron. Paris (1963).
134-35 John L. Seubert, "Biological studies of the problem of bird hazard to aircraft." *Ibid.*
135 U. S. Environmental Protection Agency, *Land Disposal Sites Near Airports Reporting Bird/Aircraft Hazards.* Washington, 1971.
135-36 James Morse (Federal Aviation Administration), personal communication.
136 U.S. Air Force, *USAF Bird Strike Summary.* Norton AFB, California, 1971.
140 Drury, "A study of Herring Gull populations."
142 William H. Drury and I. C. T. Nisbet, "Strategy of management of a natural population: the Herring Gull in New England." *Proc. World Conf. Bird Hazards to Aircraft.* Kingston, Ontario, 1969.
142-43 Frank Gramlich, personal communication.

Chapter 16

146 ff. William H. Drury and W. John Smith, "Defense of feeding areas by adult Herring Gulls and intrusion by young." *Evolution,* 22:193–201 (1968).

Chapter 17

153–54 U.S. Environmental Protection Agency, *Land Disposal Sites.*

155 I. C. T. Nisbet, "Laughing Gull colonies in the North East." *Massachusetts Audubon* (March 1971).

156 William H. Drury and John A. Kadlec, "The current status of

the Herring Gull population in the northeastern United States." *Bird-Banding,* 45:297–306 (1974).

156–58 Jack P. Hailman, "Herring Gull extends breeding range south to North Carolina." *Auk,* 80:375–376 (1963).

158 James F. Parnell and Robert F. Soots, "Herring and Great Black-backed Gulls nesting in North Carolina." *Auk,* 92:154–157 (1975).

158 D. M. Forsythe, *An Ecological Study of Gull Populations to Reduce the Bird-Aircraft Strike Hazard at Charleston Air Force Base.* Air Force Weapons Lab. Tech. Report 73–142, 1974.

Index